Mama MOVES IN

5½ Years of Eldercare in My Home

Thomas A. Dyke

Dyke Publishing Company

Austin, Texas

ISBN-13: 978-0-9842501-0-3
ISBN-10: 0-9842501-0-7
Library of Congress Control Number: 2010921931

Dyke Publishing Company
5916 Fairlane Drive
Austin, Texas 78757
Tel: 512-923-4797
www.dykepublishing.com

Cover Design by Janice Phelps Williams: www.janicephelps.com

PRINTED IN THE UNITED STATES OF AMERICA

Disclaimer

This book is written to provide information, accounts and research tools to help you decide whether to move an elderly relative into your home and to help with eldercare, if you do. It is sold with the understanding that the author and publisher are not engaged in providing medical advice, legal advice or any other professional service. For medical, legal and any other professional advice, contact an expert in the fields of medicine, law, accounting or any other professional field pertaining to the professional advice you might need.

This book was written with the intention of sharing the experiences and efforts of the author to cope with the demands of moving an elderly parent or loved one into their home. It was written for all who are either considering moving an elderly loved one into their home, or who have already moved an elderly parent or loved one into their home.

This book includes—both in print and on CD—an organized listing of linked internet sites used by the author as research resources. The author accessed many of them to help him understand and deal with his mother's behavior and symptoms as well as his own emotions and needs from the time Mama Jus moved into his home until her passing five and one-half years later.

The internet site references and links are included to save the reader time and effort in dealing with the demands of providing eldercare. You may use the CD in your computer and quickly link to subjects and products of interest and the results are always current.

This book is not an exhaustive study of eldercare either as an in-home provider or otherwise. Nothing can take the place of your doctor, nurse, physical therapist, attorney, accountant or other professional service providers.

If you do not accept the warnings and disclaimers stated above, you may return this book to the publisher for a full refund.

David Dyke and Mama Jus, 1996

Table of Contents

Introduction

Changing Relationships

The relationship between a parent and a child is established over many, many years. The love and respect one develops for a parent is entrenched before one moves out of the family home. When one grows older and establishes his or her own family with a spouse and children, the primary focus is on your own household. Visits to see parents, whether often or not, perpetuate the original relationship of love and respect for a parent. The idea of "parent" in a child's mind, regardless of that child's age, is the overarching concept that persists until that point in time when everything changes and the parent becomes dependent on the child. One knows that the day will come, but little more is paid to that eventuality than lip service.

Then it happens.

At the point of realization the child knows the roles are reversing, but often the parent does not. The transition is not always smooth and easy—especially when emotions flair for all involved. Frankly, at times there are resentments on both sides. The parent does not want to lose his or her independence and be treated as a child, and the child does not want to assume the duties of parent. *What has happened? This is my mom (or dad) who is acting this way—and I should not have to be arguing with them or reprimanding them. This is backward!* (You *will* have these thoughts.)

It is the making of the "executive" decisions, with or without discussion, that can lead to misgivings and hurt feelings. Add to that the need to direct behavior according to what is appropriate for the circumstance: "It's 25° outside and, yes, too cold for you to go out." Or, "You can't come into the room with just your Pampers on!" Yes, it gets to that point.

In addition to the reversal of management in the family comes an array of disorders and diseases peculiar to the elderly. What do you know about diet and exercise for the elderly, or incontinence and stroke as well as a whole host of other "surprises" that will surely come your way? My guess is that other than general knowledge, you do not know everything that you should know to be able to offer your parent the eldercare they need and deserve. I confess that I did not have the knowledge when I needed it, and I was slow to get ahead of the learning curve. Eventually, I did, but it could have been so much easier on everyone. And I could have, *should have*, been so much better prepared.

By reading *Mama Moves In*, you get to be a "fly-on-the-wall." You'll read about a number of experiences, most (if not all) that you will encounter, too. I'm talking first-hand, as-if-you-were-there, details that everyone who cares for an elderly parent will have to face in one form or another. Whether it's the first time Mama Jus got lost, or when she accused me of starving her, or when she fell in the shower and overflowed the drain—you can learn from my mistakes. Some of our family's stories are funny and some are sad, but all are true.

Also, within the pages of *Mama Moves In,* you will get the full benefit of my years of internet research: organized and categorized internet sites covering just about every topic you will need in preparing for, as well as caring for, your elderly parent: Alcohol and Alzheimer's to Emotions, Insomnia and Medicare to Long-Term Care, Stroke and Vision, plus many, many more—all of them are on the *InformationResearchPro–ProductResearchPro* CD enclosed with this book.

Being prepared will make your job so much easier than it was for me. And that's the reason for this book—**to make your job easier!** This is your chance to honor your parent for the years of loving care they gave you as a child, so make the most of it. Read the experiences (I call them "happenings") closely and make good use of the internet sites that will be found for you so you can take the best possible care of your loved one.

ISBN: 978-0-9842501-0-3

www.dykepublishing.com

ResearchPro ~ ProductResearchPro

InformationResearchPro

Mama MOVES IN

About the CD:

A Wealth of Information and Assistance

Included with *Mama Moves In* is your *Information-ResearchPro–ProductResearchPro* CD: an organized research tool that accesses websites in 45+ categories. Since the searches will be handled using the CD, the number of categories and accessible sites are dynamic and can expand as more information becomes available, in other words, your copy of the CD will always be current. As of publication of this book, the existing categories are:

> *Alcohol, Alzheimer's and Dementia, Anger, Arthritis, Asset Management, Bank Accounts and Banking, Bedsores, Blogs, Bowel Dysfunction, Brain Fitness and Neuroplasticity, Cancer, Caregiver, Caregiving, Constipation, Dental, Depression, Diabetes, Diet, Dementia, Driving, Drugs and Drug Plan Benefits, Dysphagia, Education, Eldercare, Eldercare Blogs, Elderly's Diseases, Emotions, Exercise, Eyesight, Feelings of the*

Caregiver, Hearing, Hispanic–Problems Peculiar to Hispanics, Humor, Incontinence and Constipation, Insomnia, Insurance Products, Internet, Law, Living Wills, Long-Term Care, Medicaid, Medicare, Medigap (Medicare Supplemental), Mental Health, Music and the Elderly, Neuroplasticity, Products for the Elderly, Prostate Disorder, Safety, Senior Citizens, Skin, Smoking, Social Security Benefits, Spirituality, Stroke, Swallowing Disorder, Toenails, Urinary Tract Infection, Vision, Wills/Trusts

Using your CD, you have quick access to all of my research as well as new information as it becomes available. With the click of your mouse, you can go directly to any category and find articles by doctors, researchers, teachers and other professionals on all of the appropriate categories listed above.

Also, you can click on the category, "Products for the Elderly" and find a number of commercial websites that sell *hundreds* of items from backscratchers and bedpans to motorized wheelchairs. You can find very clever products that will help you and your loved one. The products are organized in categories and subcategories, so it's easy to find what you are looking for. And, you can buy them and have them delivered to your door. There are a number of competing sites, so you can shop around and get the best buy.

Chapter 1
Meet Mama Jus

The information in this book, and the reason I came to write it, stems from the real experiences of people just like you and your family. The following biographical sketch is included for several reasons: First, you get to know Mama Jus' family background; second, it introduces personality traits that come into play during Mama Jus' elder-care; third, it will help you anticipate what to expect from your loved one based on her personality and your family's history; and fourth, it will help you recognize the signs that it's time to start thinking about where your loved one will live their last years.

Justine Elizabeth Pattillo (Mama Jus) was born September 10, 1910, in Orange, Texas, to Maude Bell and June Pattillo. June's parents immigrated to the Orange area in the middle 1800s. Their Irish name was Pataluc, but to avoid the perceived stigma of being "Irish," great grandfather Pataluc changed his family name to Pattillo while many immigrating here from Italy and Sicily "Americanized" their names to avoid the perceived stigma of being Italian—funny stuff, but real nonetheless based on the very personal feelings of the day. June's family lived an austere existence arguably based on Benjamin Franklin's oft quoted phrase, "A penny saved is a penny earned."

Maude Bell was of English descent and was born in East Texas near the town of Timpson. She was taught to cook East-Texas style, and she passed much of her East-Texas culinary art to her daughter, Justine (Mama Jus).

Justine's husband, Frank Jeff Dyke, was the third of five boys and was born near Castleberry, Alabama. Frank's Dad, Joe Dyke, was of English descent and worked for a series of railroad companies, primarily as a telegrapher. Frank's Mom, Lucy Love Burt Dyke, was of English descent and from Florida. She was a great Southern-style cook and passed her culinary skills on to Mama Jus, too.

It should be noted that railroad telegraphers made a subsistence living, so any enjoyment from food came in the way it was prepared, and my grandmother Lucy was a pro. Feeding six hungry males every day made "doing it right" imperative, and she did. Included in their fare was squirrel, duck, venison, hog, quail, dove and an assortment of fish. Hunting and fishing for the Dykes was not a leisure sport—success meant the difference between meat on the table or just vegetables and cornbread. Lucy made the most of everything they brought home by putting her Southern touch on every ingredient.

Justine had big, beautiful dark-brown eyes and a full head of raven black hair. She inherited her mother's sweet and gentle disposition. She reached maturity at age sixteen, was buxom, five-foot three-inches tall, weighed 102 pounds, and was sought after by just about every healthy male in the county. *The Orange Peal,* Orange High's yearbook, confirms that she was given the title of "Prettiest Girl."

Though "protected" by two adoring younger brothers, Sam and Junius, Justine could take care of herself. She was tough in a gentle sort of way.

When she was about ten years old the family lived on the edge of town. They had a few cows, two horses, chickens, and an assortment of critters adopted from time to time by her brothers. As a part of minding the livestock, bails of hay were kept in a loft over the barn floor. Of course, a haying fork was kept near the entrance to the barn. One morning, Justine was rounding one corner of the barn in a full run, and her brother Sam was coming from the other direction pushing the hay fork ahead of him. They met at the corner and one of the tines of the fork entered Justine's left foot between her big toe and its neighbor. The doctor said that it was fortunate that the tine made it all the way through her foot and out of her heal. It made cleaning and dressing her wound much easier, and probably kept her from losing her foot. Uncle Sam told me she never shed a tear, but was concerned that Sam and the rest of the family were so upset. This is what I mean by tough, but gentle and kind.

June, Mama Jus' dad, provided for his family with his modest earnings by being very frugal. Mama Jus once related a childhood story to me. After school one

Justine Pattillo — Prettiest Girl, 1927

day she walked about a mile from school to her dad's office in downtown Orange. She wanted to get a nickel from him so she could join her friends at the drugstore for a Coke. He refused her and lectured on expecting something for nothing. She ended the story by telling me she never asked him for anything again.

Justine had been courted by Frank Dyke before she left for college. After one semester of college in New Orleans, Justine returned to Orange. That was all the family could afford.

Frank Dyke was a six-footer, had wavy, strawberry blond hair, and led a Dixieland Band. He was hard working and knew what he wanted. He was putting himself through the University of Texas with the proceeds from his band, delivering newspapers early in the mornings, and working tables at the boarding house. He knew that Justine was returning to Orange, so he did, too—before getting his degree.

After a brief continuation of his courtship of Justine, they were married. He took a job with Gulf States Utilities in Beaumont, Texas. Not long after that they moved to Lake Charles, Louisiana, where he was promoted into Gulf State's advertising department. Frank had found his niche.

After another two years with Gulf States, Frank and Justine moved back to Beaumont, Texas, and he opened his own industrial advertising firm. Their first son, Jeff, was born to them in Beaumont, January 22, 1935. After another two years in Beaumont, Frank moved his family to Houston, Texas, to take advantage of a much larger advertising market.

Jeff, Mama Jus, Tom and David, 1943

New companies were being formed to service the rapidly growing oil industry, and Frank's instincts told him opportunities would be much greater in Houston than in Beaumont. During the next twenty-five years he grew the business into a substantial industrial advertising firm.

During those years, Mom was managing the house, the bank account and Jeff. Her next son, David Fletcher, was born March 9, 1938, and her youngest, Tom, was born October 1, 1940. Preparing all of the meals and keeping three rambunctious boys in clothes, taking them to all of their sports activities, and making sure the house was always neat and clean, kept her busy full time. Home life was great for all of us.

In 1938 Frank purchased a new home for his family in West University, a middle class neighborhood near Rice University. Then in 1952, Frank moved his family into a new home in Tanglewood, an upper middle-class neighborhood on the west side of Houston. Again, it was great for all of us. There was more room and Mama Jus had a much bigger kitchen where she could work her magic.

In the summer of 1956, Mama Jus did something she had never done before—she took a trip with her longtime friend Marvel to Hawaii. Marvel was just the opposite of Justine. She'd go anywhere anytime without her husband, Charlie. It took months for Marvel to convince Mom that her family could get along without her for two weeks, but in late May, Marvel won the argument and Justine announced to us that she was going to Hawaii. None of us believed it until she bought her airplane tickets, but we were glad that she was getting her first real vacation since her first child was born in 1935.

After Mom was gone for nearly two weeks, we received a postcard telling us that she had decided to stretch her vacation another *two weeks*. She was having fun, had caught a large sailfish, had taken a ride on an outrigger canoe, and was learning to hula. She signed her card, "Love, Mama Jus." Later we found out that the young Hawaiian who served as their guide had given her the name, Mama Jus. It is traditional in Hawaii for kids to precede their mom's given name with Mama, hence, the young Hawaiian guide showed his affection and respect for Mom by calling her Mama Jus. It stuck for the rest of her life.

In keeping with the tradition of the era, Frank was definitely the head of the house. He controlled most of the money, and made most of the major family decisions. He taught his boys to hunt and fish, and took all of us regularly to bountiful hunting and fishing spots in Texas and elsewhere. Mom always stayed at home, and had one of her excellent, Southern-style meals ready for us when we returned.

Having learned from two of the best, Mama Jus was quite a cook. She got the best of training in Southern cooking, in general, and East Texas cooking, in particular. All of our friends took advantage of every opportunity to eat a meal at our house. But Mama Jus was not just a great cook; she was also an understanding listener. Every time any of us boys hosted a party in our home, many of our friends would gather in the kitchen and talk to Mama Jus—she had a great ear.

Several years after I graduated from college, Frank and Mama Jus moved into a home they built a few miles just north of Brookshire, Texas. It was on fifty acres of Brazos River bottom land and was covered with pecan trees. Some of the old trees measured nearly twenty-five feet in circumference. They had a pool, a barn down by the stock pond Dad built, and Irons Creek running along the back of the property. They spent nearly ten peaceful years at the country place before they lost their firstborn in a plane crash.

It was a tragic loss for all of us, and shortly after Jeff's death, they moved to Austin, Texas, to be near their son, Tom, and good medical facilities. Their home in Austin was very comfortable. It had a gourmet kitchen, and a beautiful sawed limestone fireplace that reached to the ceiling. The limestone was full of fossils, and their grandchildren loved discovering the Nautili.

They hadn't been in Austin long when Dad had his first micro stroke. It did no lasting damage, but was a precursor to what was coming. After just three years in Austin, Dad decided he wanted to be back in a more rural setting. He arrived home one afternoon and informed Mama Jus that he had bought a home near Richmond, Texas, and that they were moving. She did not appreciate not being consulted in any way about the move, but went along to keep the peace. But she didn't mind telling me about her feelings, and I didn't mind listening—she was my Mama Jus.

They hadn't been in their new home long when Mama Jus announced that she was no longer going to

Above: Mama Jus on the front porch of their country home, 1978

Below: Frank Dyke, 1978

be the cook—she was through. Dad grumped, but he knew he had enjoyed better home cooking than anyone he knew. Dad was not a bad cook himself, so it wasn't a total disaster. Mama Jus had retired!

Dad had another micro stroke shortly after they moved into their new home, but again, it did no observable damage. Mama Jus and Dad rocked along for another two years, and then Dad had another stroke that did some damage. His speech would break up after he got the first couple of words out, and his writing was similarly affected. But his physical health was good. He was a strong man, and his personal strength carried him on until a devastating stroke hit him in early December 1990. Mama Jus cared for him the best she could, but the medical attention that he required was beyond her capabilities. She was lost. The man she had depended on for so many years was laid low. Dad was hospitalized with massive clots in his legs, unable to talk, and was bedridden until his death two weeks later. His final hour came December 26, 1989. Mama Jus was alone.

It didn't take much to convince Mama Jus to look at retirement homes in Austin. She selected Austin's best retirement mid-rise, Westminster Manor. Fortunately it was just a few blocks from my home. Mom chose her unit and we contracted to have the interior design work completed to her satisfaction. The movers packaged her furniture and furnishings, and moved her from the Ft. Bend area south of Houston to Austin. Having a couple with whom she had been friends for fifty years already at Westminster didn't hurt, and it wasn't long before she had settled into her new spot. She could smoke in her condo, and she had friends with whom she could enjoy her five o'clock toddy. Her preferences were Salem Lights and Vodka.

See InformationResearchPro CD Categories:
Alcohol and Smoking

Although Mama Jus had a serviceable car and was a good driver, she quickly decided that the drivers in Austin were crazy and that she no longer needed to drive. Westminster offered a private shuttle bus to the grocery stores and to other destinations when given notice. Between the shuttle, family assistance, and Westminster's maids, Mom had easy access to her choice of grocery items, sundries and destinations.

See InformationResearchPro CD Categories:
Driving

After some time, my wife, Sibyl, and I decided to move Mama Jus into our home. We felt she would be more comfortable there. On the day that I told Mrs. Johnson, the director at Westminster, that I had decided to sell Mama Jus' condo and move her into our home, she said, "Get ready for a rough and extended adjustment period."

I was quick to respond with, "Oh don't worry, we have been talking about it for some time, and Mom is ready for the move."

Mrs. Johnson then made herself clear, "Mr. Dyke, I am not talking about your mother. I am talking about *you*."

I smiled obligingly and wondered to myself what on earth she meant by that. As it turned out, her pre-science was remarkable.

By the end of the second year after Mama Jus moved in with us, it was clear that I might have bitten off more than I could chew. I had not prepared for the challenges of caring for an elderly parent. The time demands, the physical demands, the information demands and the emotional demands almost buried me. But for my wife, a couple of great doctors and a lot of behind-the-curve research, I might not have made it. I played "catch up" for the first two years, and then life got a little easier.

This little book is designed to help you prepare ahead of time and give you ready access to the information that you will need. The enclosed CD will take you lightning-fast to the answers and products you will need from day-to-day.

Above: Frank Dyke with the author's sons, Tommy and Will Rob, 1969. Below: Mama Jus, Tom Dyke, Tommy and Will Rob, going for a ride in the old Model T., 1973

Chapter 2

Our Home or the Rest Home

Whether the reason for moving an elderly parent or relative into your home is financial/economics or just the desire to care for your loved one in your home, you have much to consider and discuss with other siblings and relatives *before* taking such an important step.

Costs Associated with Elder-Care

Assuming the economy or a financial setback has left you with no other option than to move your loved one into your home, you should take steps to ease the load in every way you can. First, determine exactly what the increase in your monthly costs will be after the move in. Plan generously for additional food, a minimal amount of added utilities, an adequate supply of senior diapers (they will be needed at some point), regular sitters (so you can have some time to yourself), medical treatment, over-the-counter medicines and entertainment.

Know that the needed prescription drugs will likely increase, so explore your options: Is your loved one covered under Medicare Parts A and B, and is a

Medicare drug plan included? If there is no Medicare Part B, discuss with your insurance carrier the costs of adding Part B. If they do not have a drug plan, discuss adding that coverage, too.

> *See InformationResearchPro CD Categories: Medicare, Medigap, Drugs and Drug Plans*

After you have all of the costs that you can anticipate will have to be covered, assess the income available from *all* sources. First, consider any retirement benefits, social security benefits, and any other income and assets your loved one has available to match against the costs. A home or other assets can be sold and the cash can be applied against the costs. If your loved one can cover all costs, that's great and you can concentrate on the other demands of care giving. If your loved one does not have the required income and assets to cover all additional costs, you should take immediate steps to include as many family members as possible to defray all uncovered costs.

> *See InformationResearchPro CD Categories: Social Security Benefits*

I suggest that you arrange a meeting, in person, with all of your family members to discuss and determine whether they can assume some of the responsibility or not. "Moral suasion" works better in person than over the telephone or by email; however, email can work and it gives you a record if you need it later. (Remember: It's harder to say no when someone is looking you in the eye.) Those who cannot attend the meeting should be included by conference call. The more participation you encourage in the planning from other relatives the more likely they will participate in covering the costs not covered by your loved one. The best procedure includes a personal meeting followed by emails, if available, to confirm the agreement. Save any relevant emails for use later if you need them—it could make a difference in getting the help you'll need.

There are several ways for family members to participate. Cash is the obvious way, but *time* and *in-kind items* like clothing, produce, eggs and poultry, and other items that one or more of the family members produce are wonderful—anything that helps spread the costs.

Regardless, let the family know just what the costs are. Also, let them know what it would cost for eldercare outside of your home for commercial facilities, drugs, doctors and other health-care providers.

With all of the costs on the table, your relatives will be more likely to do their part rather than leave you with the entire burden of in-home elder-care.

Time, often overlooked, is a major consideration. I can tell you that without help from others, whether for hire or from other family members, you will find that you no longer have a life of your own. You should, if at all possible, arrange for time to be contributed by as many relatives as possible for weekly respite care and for vacation time of at least two weeks annually—four to six weeks spread over time would be much better. When you are on duty, it will be 24/7.

Soliciting, discussing and securing commitments before your loved one moves in is a must. If you do not make the arrangements before the move-in date, you may likely be left will little or no help. Left figuring it all out on your own, you will experience a broad range of emotions that are damaging to everyone— your loved one, your relatives and yourself.

MEDICAID, MEDICARE, MEDIGAP (MEDICARE SUPPLEMENTAL) AND LONG-TERM CARE

Insurance: Medicaid, Medicare, Medigap (Medicare Supplemental)

Qualifications for the receipt of Medicaid, Medicare and Medicare Supplemental are case specific; in other words the vetting process that determines eligibility is dependent on individual factors and outside the scope of this book to determine.

Medicaid is funded by the federal government, but administered by state agencies. Medicare is funded *and* administered by the federal government, and Medicare Supplemental is sold and administered by private insurance companies. Since all of the governments' (federal and state) details concerning qualifications, costs, coverages and administration are case specific for each plan, I refer you to the internet sites listed under each category in the enclosed CD.

I strongly suggest that you thoroughly familiarize yourself with the information available at each of the sites before making decisions. Additionally, I suggest you consult with an expert in the field, your CPA, attorney or qualified insurance representative before making any decisions.

See InformationResearchPro CD Categories:
Medicaid, Medicare and Medigap

Long-Term Care Insurance

Long-Term Care is another insurance policy that covers long-term elder-care. A number of factors are considered to establish what to buy: the type, the term, the amount, the geographical location and the age and health of the prospective insured.

Listed below are elder-care cost categories for levels of care that you should consider:

Nursing Home

Private Room _____

Semi-Private Room _____

Assisted Living Facility

Private One Bedroom _____

Adult Day-Care Facility _____

(8 Hours per Day, 5 Days per Week)

Adult Day-Care _____

Home Care

(Home Health Aid)(44 Hours per Week)

Medicare-Certified & Licensed _____

Licensed Only _____

(Homemaker Services)(44 Hours per Week)

Licensed Only _____

See InformationResearchPro CD Categories:
Long-Term Care

Genworth Financial has generously consented to allowing the inclusion of its researched cost data for elder-care gathered from most major cities and towns in the United States.

Also, Genworth has allowed you direct access from the enclosed CD to the Genworth Financial web site so you can quickly and easily determine the cost of any particular level of Long-Term Care that you might be considering for your loved one (or yourself).

Visit:

www.genworth.com/content/products/long_term_care.html

(A link to this site is provided at dykepublishing.com and on the enclosed CD.)

Tip for Using the Genworth Financial Map of the United States:

Place your computer's cursor over your state and click. You will have access to cost data in many cities and towns within your state as well as the median costs for the cities not listed. It is a great tool.

(Genworth updates the numbers annually.)

Chapter 3:

Home Safety Checklist

A lthough the following checklist was prepared by the Consumer Product Safety Commission (CPSC), based on data from as early as 1981, it is still germane today. You may complete the checklist to help you prepare for moving an elderly parent or relative into your home.

No list is ever complete, however, so use common sense and good judgment to make additions to your list.

Note: At the time of our publication, the CPSC was in the process of assembling an updated version of the checklist that follows in this book. Check with the always-current link in the enclosed InformationResearchPro CD for the release of the CPSC's new list.

HOME SAFETY CHECKLIST

COURTESY OF
U.S. CONSUMER PRODUCT SAFETY COMMISSION

Each year, many older Americans are injured in and around their homes. The U.S. Consumer Product Safety Commission (CPSC) estimates that in 1981, over 622,000 people over age 65 were treated in hospital emergency rooms for injuries associated with products they live with and use everyday.

CPSC believes that many of these injuries result from hazards that are easy to overlook, but also easy to fix. By spotting these hazards and taking some simple steps to correct them, many injuries might be prevented.

Use this checklist to spot possible safety problems which may be present in your home. Check YES or NO to answer each question. Then go back over the list and take action to correct those items which may need attention.

Keep this checklist as a reminder of safe practices, and use it periodically to re-check your home.

This checklist is organized by areas in the home. However, there are some potential hazards that need to be checked in more than just one area of your home.

These are highlighted at the beginning of the checklist and short reminders are included in each other section of the checklist.

ALL AREAS OF THE HOME

In all areas of your home, check all electrical and telephone cords; rugs, runners and mats; telephone areas; smoke detectors; electrical outlets and switches; light bulbs; space heaters; wood-burning stoves; and your emergency exit plan.

✓ Check All Cords

QUESTION: Are lamp, extension, and telephone cords placed out of the flow of traffic?

_____YES   _____NO

RECOMMENDATION:

❑ Cords stretched across walkways may cause someone to trip.

❑ Arrange furniture so that outlets are available for lamps and appliances without the use of extension cords.

❑ If you must use an extension cord, place it on the floor against a wall where people can not trip over it.

❑ Move the phone so that telephone cords will not lie where people walk.

QUESTION: Are cords out from beneath furniture and rugs or carpeting?

_____YES   _____NO

RECOMMENDATION: Furniture resting on cords can damage them, creating fire and shock hazards. Electric cords which run under carpeting may cause a fire.

❑ Remove cords from under furniture or carpeting.

❑ Replace damaged or frayed cords.

QUESTION: Are cords attached to the walls, baseboards, etc., with nails or staples?

____YES   ____NO

Nails or staples can damage cords, presenting fire and shock hazards.

RECOMMENDATION:

❏   Remove nails, staples, etc.

❏   Check wiring for damage.

❏   Use tape to attach cords to walls or floors.

QUESTION: Are electrical cords in good condition, not frayed or cracked?

____YES   ____NO

Damaged cords may cause a shock or fire.

RECOMMENDATION:

❏   Replace frayed or cracked cords.

QUESTION: Do extension cords carry more than their proper load, as indicated by the ratings labeled on the cord and the appliance?

____YES   ____NO

Overloaded extension cords may cause fires. Standard 18 gauge extension cords can carry 1250 watts.

RECOMMENDATION:

❏   If the rating on the cord is exceeded because of the power requirements of one or more appliances being used on the cord, change the cord to a higher rated one or unplug some appliances.

❏   If an extension cord is needed, use one having a sufficient amp or wattage rating.

✓ Check All Rugs, Runners and Mats

QUESTION: Are all small rugs and runners slip-resistant?

____YES   ____NO

CPSC estimates that in 1982, over 2,500 people 65 and over were treated in hospital emergency rooms for injuries that resulted from tripping over rugs and runners. Falls are also the most common cause of fatal injury for older people.

RECOMMENDATION:

❒ Remove rugs and runners that tend to slide.

❒ Apply double-faced adhesive carpet tape or rubber matting to the backs of rugs and runners.

❒ Purchase rugs with slip-resistant backing.

❒ Check rugs and mats periodically to see if backing needs to be replaced.

❒ Place rubber matting under rugs. (Rubber matting that can be cut to size is available.)

❒ Purchase new rugs with slip-resistant backing.

NOTE: Over time, adhesive on tape can wear away. Rugs with slip- resistant backing also become less effective as they are washed. Periodically, check rugs and mats to see if new tape or backing is needed.

QUESTION: Are emergency numbers posted on or near the telephone?

____YES   ____NO

RECOMMENDATION: In case of emergency, telephone numbers for the Police, Fire Department, and local Poison Control Center, along with a neighbor's number, should be readily available.

❒ Write the numbers in large print and tape them to the phone, or place them near the phone where they can be seen easily.

QUESTION: Do you have access to a telephone if you fall (or experience some other emergency which prevents you from standing and reaching a wall phone)?

_____YES   _____NO

RECOMMENDATION:

❐   Have at least one telephone located where it would be accessible in the event of an accident which leaves you unable to stand.

✓ Check Smoke Detectors

QUESTION: Are smoke detectors properly located?

_____YES   _____NO

RECOMMENDATION:

❐   At least one smoke detector should be placed on every floor of your home.

❐   Read the instructions that come with the smoke detector for advice on the best place to install it.

❐   Make sure detectors are placed near bedrooms, either on the ceiling or 6-12 inches below the ceiling on the wall.

❐   Locate smoke detectors away from air vents.

QUESTION: Do you have properly working smoke detectors?

_____YES   _____NO

RECOMMENDATION: Many home fire injuries and deaths are caused by smoke and toxic gases, rather than the fire itself. Smoke detectors provide an early warning and can wake you in the event of a fire.

❐   Purchase a smoke detector if you do not have one.

❐   Check and replace batteries and bulbs according to the manufacturer's instructions.

❒ Vacuum the grillwork of your smoke detector.

❒ Replace any smoke detectors which can not be repaired.

NOTE: Some fire departments or local governments will provide assistance in acquiring or installing smoke detectors.

✓ Check Electrical Outlets and Switches

QUESTION: Are any outlets and switches unusually warm or hot to the touch?

_____YES   _____NO

Unusually warm or hot outlets or switches may indicate that an unsafe wiring condition exists.

RECOMMENDATION:

❒ Unplug cords from outlets and do not use the switches.

❒ Have an electrician check the wiring as soon as possible.

QUESTION: Do all outlets and switches have cover plates, so that no wiring is exposed?

_____YES   _____NO

RECOMMENDATION: Exposed wiring presents a shock hazard.

❒ Add a cover plate.

QUESTION: Are light bulbs the appropriate size and type for the lamp or fixture?

_____YES   _____NO

RECOMMENDATION: A bulb of too high wattage or the wrong type may lead to fire through overheating. Ceiling fixtures, recessed lights, and "hooded" lamps will trap heat.

❒ Replace with a bulb of the correct type and wattage. (If you do not know the correct wattage, use a bulb no larger than 60 watts.)

✓ Check Space Heaters

QUESTION: Are heaters which come with a 3-prong plug being used in a 3-hole outlet or with a properly attached adapter?

_____YES   _____NO

RECOMMENDATION: The grounding feature provided by a 3-hole receptacle or an adapter for a 2-hole receptacle is a safety feature designed to lessen the risk of shock.

❒ Never defeat the grounding feature.

❒ If you do not have a 3-hole outlet, use an adapter to connect the heater's 3-prong plug. Make sure the adapter ground wire or tab is attached to the outlet.

QUESTION: Are small stoves and heaters placed where they can not be knocked over, and away from furnishings and flammable materials, such as curtains or rugs?

_____YES   _____NO

RECOMMENDATION: Heaters can cause fires or serious burns if they cause you to trip or if they are knocked over.

❒ Relocate heaters away from passageways and flammable materials such as curtains, rugs, furniture, etc.

QUESTION: If your home has space heating equipment, such as a kerosene heater, a gas heater or an LP gas heater, do you understand the installation and operating instructions thoroughly?

_____YES   _____NO

RECOMMENDATION: Unvented heaters should be used with room doors open or window slightly open to provide ventilation. The correct fuel, as recommended by the manufacturer, should always be used. Vented heaters should have proper venting, and the venting system should be checked frequently. Improper venting is the most frequent cause of carbon monoxide poisoning, and older consumers are at special risk.

❑   Review the installation and operating instructions.

Call your local fire department if you have additional questions.

✓ Check Woodburning Heating Equipment

QUESTION: Is wood burning equipment installed properly?

_____YES   _____NO

RECOMMENDATION:

❑   Wood burning stoves should be installed by a qualified person according to local building codes.

❑   Local building code officials or fire marshals can provide requirements and recommendations for installation.

NOTE: Some insurance companies will not cover fire losses if wood stoves are not installed according to local codes.

✓ Check the Emergency Exit Plan

QUESTION: Do you have an emergency exit plan and an alternate emergency exit plan in case of a fire?

_____YES   _____NO

RECOMMENDATION: Once a fire starts, it spreads rapidly. Since you may not have much time to get out and there may be a lot of confusion, it is important that everyone knows what to do.

❑   Develop an emergency exit plan.

- ❐ Choose a meeting place outside your home so you can be sure that everyone is capable of escape quickly and safely.
- ❐ Practice the plan from time to time to make sure everyone is capable of escape quickly and safely.
- ❐ <u>Remember periodically to re-check your home.</u>

KITCHEN

In the kitchen, check the range area, all electrical cords, lighting, the stool, all throw rugs and mats, and the telephone area.

✓ Check the Range Area

QUESTION: Are towels, curtains, and other things that might catch fire located away from the range?

____YES   ____NO

RECOMMENDATION: Placing or storing non-cooking equipment like potholders, dish towels, or plastic utensils on or near the range man result in fires or burns.

- ❐ Store flammable and combustible items away from range and oven.
- ❐ Remove any towels hanging on oven handles. If towels hang close to a burner, change the location of the towel rack.
- ❐ If necessary, shorten or remove curtains which could brush against heat sources.

QUESTION: Do you wear clothing with short or close-fitting sleeves while you are cooking?

____YES   ____NO

RECOMMENDATION: CPSC estimates that 70% of all people who die from clothing fires are over 65 years of age. Long sleeves are more likely to catch fire than are short sleeves. Long sleeves are also more apt to catch on pot handles, overturning pots and pans and causing scalds.

☐ Roll back long, loose sleeves or fasten them with pins or elastic bands while you are cooking.

QUESTION: Are kitchen ventilation systems or range exhausts functioning properly and are they in use while you are cooking?

____YES   ____NO

RECOMMENDATION: Indoor air pollutants may accumulate to unhealthful levels in a kitchen where gas or kerosene-fire appliances are in use.

☐ Use ventilation systems or open windows to clear air of vapors and smoke.

QUESTION: Are all extension cords and appliance cords located away from the sink or range areas?

____YES   ____NO

RECOMMENDATION: Electrical appliances and power cords can cause shock or electrocution if they come in contact with water. Cords can also be damaged by excess heat.

☐ Move cords and appliances away from sink areas and hot surfaces.

☐ Move appliances closer to wall outlets or to different outlets so you won't need extension cords.

☐ If extension cords must be used, install wiring guides so that cords will not hang near sink, range, or working areas.

☐ Consider adding new outlets for convenience and safety; ask your electrician to install outlets equipped with ground fault circuit interrupters (GFCI's) to protect against electric shock. A GFCI is a shock-protection device that will detect electrical fault and shut off electricity before serious injury or death occurs.

❏ For more information on cords, refer to the beginning of the checklist.

QUESTION: Does good, even lighting exist over the stove, sink, and countertop work areas, especially where food is sliced or cut?

_____YES   _____NO

RECOMMENDATION: Low lighting and glare can contribute to burns or cuts. Improve lighting by:

❏ Opening curtains and blinds (unless this causes too much glare).

❏ Using the maximum wattage bulb allowed by the fixture. (If you do not know the correct wattage for the fixture, use a bulb no larger than 60 watts.)

❏ Reducing glare by using frosted bulbs, indirect lighting, shades or globes on light fixtures, or partially closing the blinds or curtains.

❏ Installing additional light fixtures, e.g. under cabinet/over countertop lighting.

❏ (Make sure that the bulbs you use are the right type and wattage for the light fixture.)

✓ Step Stools / Ladders

QUESTION: Do you have a step stool which is stable and in good repair?

_____YES   _____NO

RECOMMENDATION: Standing on chairs, boxes, or other makeshift items to reach high shelves and light bulbs can result in falls. CPSC estimates that in 1982, 1500 people over 65 were treated in hospital emergency rooms when they fell from chairs on which they were standing.

❏ If you don't have a step stool, consider buying one. Choose one with a handrail that you can hold onto while standing on the top step.

☐ Before climbing on any step stool, make sure it is fully opened and stable.

☐ Tighten screws and braces on the step stool.

☐ Discard step stools with broken parts.

☐ Remember: Check all of the product areas mentioned at the beginning of the checklist.

LIVING ROOM //FAMILY ROOM

In the living room/family room, check all rugs and runners, electrical and telephone cords, lighting, the fireplace and chimney, the telephone area, and all passageways.

QUESTION: Are chimneys clear from accumulations of leaves, and other debris that can clog them?

____YES   ____NO

RECOMMENDATION: A clogged chimney can cause a poorly-burning fire to result in poisonous fumes and smoke coming back into the house.

☐ Do not use the chimney until the blockage has been removed.

☐ Have the chimney checked and cleaned by a registered or licensed professional.

QUESTION: Has the chimney been cleaned within the past year?

____YES   ____NO

RECOMMENDATION: Burning wood can cause a build up of a tarry substance (creosote) inside the chimney. This material can ignite and result in a serious chimney fire.

❏ Have the chimney checked and cleaned by a registered or licensed professional.

✓ Check the Telephone Area

For information on the telephone area, refer to the beginning of the checklist.

✓ Check Passageways

QUESTION: Are hallways, passageways between rooms, and other heavy traffic areas well lit?

_____YES   _____NO

RECOMMENDATION: Shadowed or dark areas can hide tripping hazards.

❏ Use the maximum wattage bulb allowed by the fixture. (If you do not know the correct wattage, use a bulb no larger than 60 watts.)

❏ Install night lights.

❏ Reduce glare by using frosted bulbs, indirect lighting, shades or globes on light fixtures, or partially closing blinds or curtains.

❏ Consider using additional lamps or light fixtures. Make sure that the bulbs you use are the right type and wattage for the light fixture.

QUESTION: Are exits and passageways kept clear?

_____YES   _____NO

❏ Furniture, boxes, or other items could be an obstruction or tripping hazard, especially in the event of an emergency or fire.

❏ Rearrange furniture to open passageways and walkways.

❐ Remove boxes and clutter.

❐ Remember: Check all of the product areas mentioned at the beginning of the checklist.

BATHROOM

In the bathroom, check bathtub and shower areas, water temperature, rugs and mats, lighting, small electrical appliances, and storage areas for medications.

✓ Check Bathtub and Shower Areas

QUESTION: Are bathtubs and showers equipped with non-skid mats, abrasive strips, or surfaces that are not slippery?

_____YES   _____NO

RECOMMENDATION: Wet soapy tile or porcelain surfaces are especially slippery and may contribute to falls.

❐ Apply textured strips or appliqués on the floors of tubs and showers.

❐ Use non-skid mats in the tub and shower, and on the bathroom floor.

QUESTION: Do bathtubs and showers have at least one (preferably two) grab bars?

_____YES   _____NO

RECOMMENDATION: Grab bars can help you get into and out of your tub or shower, and can help prevent falls.

❐ Check existing bars for strength and stability, and repair if necessary.

❐ Attach grab bars, through the tile, to structural supports in the wall, or install bars specifically designed to attach to the sides of the bathtub. If you are not sure how it is done, get someone who is qualified to assist you.

47

QUESTION: Is the temperature 120 degrees or lower?

_____YES _____NO

Water temperature above 120 degrees can cause tap water scalds.

RECOMMENDATION:

❏ Lower the setting on your hot water heater to "Low" or 120 degrees. If you are unfamiliar with the controls of your water heater, ask a qualified person to adjust it for you. If your hot water system is controlled by the landlord, ask the landlord to consider lowering the setting.

NOTE: If the water heater does not have a temperature setting, you can use a thermometer to check the temperature of the water at the tap.

❏ Always check water temperature by hand before entering bath or shower.

❏ Taking baths, rather than showers, reduces the risk of a scald from suddenly changing water temperatures.

✓ Check Lighting

QUESTION: Is a light switch located near the entrance to the bathroom?

_____YES _____NO

RECOMMENDATION: A light switch near the door will prevent you from walking through a dark area.

❏ Install a night light. Inexpensive lights that plug into outlets are available.

❏ Consider replacing the existing switch with a "glow switch" that can be seen in the dark.

✓ Check Small Electrical Appliances

QUESTION: Are small electrical appliances such as hair dryers, shavers, curling irons, etc., unplugged when not in use?

_____YES _____NO

RECOMMENDATION: Even an appliance that is not turned on, such as a hairdryer, can be potentially hazardous if it is left plugged in. If it falls into water in a sink or bathtub while plugged in, it could cause a lethal shock.

❏ Unplug all small appliances when not in use.

❏ Never reach into water to retrieve an appliance that has fallen in without being sure the appliance is unplugged.

❏ Install a ground fault circuit interrupter (GFCI) in your bathroom outlet to protect against electric shock.

✓ Check Medications

QUESTION: Are all medicines stored in the containers that they came in and are they clearly marked?

_____YES _____NO

RECOMMENDATION: Medications that are not clearly and accurately labeled can be easily mixed up. Taking the wrong medicine or missing a dosage of medicine you need can be dangerous.

❏ Be sure that all containers are clearly marked with the contents, doctor's instructions, expiration date, and patient's name.

❏ Dispose of outdated medicines properly.

❏ Request non-child-resistant closures from your pharmacist only when you cannot use child-resistant closures.

NOTE: Many poisonings occur when children visiting grandparents go through the medicine cabinet or grandmother's purse. In homes where grandchildren or other youngsters are frequent visitors, medicines should be purchased in containers with child-resistant caps, and the caps properly closed after each use. Store medicines beyond the reach of children.

❑ Remember: Check all of the product areas mentioned at the beginning of the checklist.

BEDROOMS

In the bedroom, check all rugs and runners, electrical and telephone cords, and areas around beds.

✓ Check Areas around Beds

QUESTION: Are lamps or light switches within reach of each bed?

_____YES   _____NO

RECOMMENDATION: Lamps or switches located close to each bed will enable people getting up at night to see where they are going.

❑ Rearrange furniture closer to switches or move lamps closer to beds.

❑ Install night lights.

QUESTION: Are ash trays, smoking materials or other fire sources (heaters, hot plates, teapots, etc.) located away from beds or bedding?

_____YES   _____NO

RECOMMENDATION: Burns are a leading cause of accidental death among seniors. Smoking in bed is a major contributor to this problem. Among mattress and bedding fire related deaths in a recent year, 42% were to persons 65 or older.

❑ Remove sources of heat or flame from areas around beds.

❒ Don't smoke in bed.

QUESTION: Is anything covering your electric blanket when in use?

_____YES   _____NO

RECOMMENDATION: "Tucking in" electric blankets or placing additional coverings on top of them can cause excessive heat buildup which can start a fire.

QUESTION: Do you avoid "tucking in" the sides or ends of your electric blanket?

RECOMMENDATION:

❒ Use electric blankets according to the manufacturer's instructions.

❒ Don't allow anything on top of the blanket while it is in use. (This includes other blankets or comforters, even pets sleeping on top of the blanket.)

❒ Don't set electric blankets so high that they could burn someone who falls asleep while they are on.

QUESTION: Do you ever go to sleep with a heating pad which is turned on?

_____YES   _____NO

RECOMMENDATION:

❒ Never go to sleep with a heating pad if it is turned on because it can cause serious burns even at relatively low settings.

QUESTION: Is there a telephone close to your bed?

_____YES   _____NO

RECOMMENDATION: In case of an emergency, it is important to be able to reach the telephone without getting out of bed.

❏ Remember: Check all of the product areas mentioned at the beginning of the checklist.

BASEMENT / GARAGE / WORKSHOP / STORAGE AREAS

In the basement, garage, workshop, and storage areas, check lighting, fuse boxes or circuit breakers, appliances and power tools, electrical cords, and flammable liquids.

✓ Check Lighting

QUESTION: Are work areas, especially areas where power tools are used, well lit?

_____YES   _____NO

RECOMMENDATION: Power tools were involved in over 5,200 injuries treated in hospital emergency rooms to people 65 and over in 1982. Three fourths of these were finger injuries. Good lighting can reduce the chance that you will accidentally cut your finger.

❏ Either install additional light, or avoid working with power tools in the area.

QUESTION: Can you turn on the lights without first having to walk through a dark area?

_____YES   _____NO

RECOMMENDATION: Basement, garages, and storage areas can contain many tripping hazards and sharp or pointed tools that can make a fall even more hazardous.

❏ Keep an operating flashlight handy.

☐ Have an electrician install switches at each entrance to a dark area.

✓ Check the Fuse Box or Circuit Breakers

QUESTION: If fuses are used, are they the correct size for the circuit?

____YES   ____NO

RECOMMENDATION: Replacing a correct size fuse with a larger size fuse can present a serious fire hazard. If the fuse in the box is rater higher than that intended for the circuit, excessive current will be allowed to flow and possibly over-load the outlet and house wiring to the point that a fire can begin.

☐ Be certain that correct-size fuses are used. (If you do not know the correct sizes, consider having an electrician identify and label the sizes to be used.)

NOTE: If all, or nearly all, fuses used are 30-amp fuses, there is a chance that some of the fuses are rated too high for the circuit.

✓ Check Appliances and Power Tools

QUESTION: Are power tools equipped with a 3-prong plug or marked to show that they are double insulated?

____YES   ____NO

RECOMMENDATION: These safety features reduce the risk of an electric shock.

☐ Use a properly connected 3-prong adapter for connecting a 3- prong plug to a 2-hole receptacle.

☐ Consider replacing old tools that have neither a 3-prong plug nor are double insulated.

QUESTION: Are power tools guards in place?

_____YES   _____NO

RECOMMENDATION: Power tools used with guards removed pose a serious risk of injury from sharp edges or moving parts.

❏   Replace guards that have been removed from power tools.

QUESTION: Has the grounding feature on any 3-prong plug been defeated by removal of the grounding pin or by improperly using an adapter?

_____YES   _____NO

RECOMMENDATION: Improperly grounded appliances can lead to electric shock.

❏   Check with your service person or an electrician if you are in doubt.

✓   Check Flammable and Volatile Liquids

QUESTION: Are containers of volatile liquids tightly capped?

_____YES   _____NO

RECOMMENDATION: If not tightly closed, vapors may escape that may be toxic when inhaled.

❏   Check containers periodically to make sure they are tightly closed.

NOTE: CPSC has reports of several cases in which gasoline, stored as much as 10 feet from a gas water heater, exploded. Many people are unaware that gas fumes can travel that far.

QUESTION: Are gasoline, paints, solvents, or other products that give off vapors or fumes stored away from ignition sources?

_____YES   _____NO

RECOMMENDATION: Gasoline, kerosene, and other flammable liquids should be stored out of living areas in properly labeled, non- glass safety containers.

❐ Remove these products from the areas near heat or flame such as heaters, furnaces, water heaters, ranges, and other gas appliances.

✓ Stairs

For all stairways, check lighting, handrails, and the condition of the steps and coverings.

✓ Check Lighting

QUESTION: Are stairs well lighted?

_____YES   _____NO

RECOMMENDATION: Stairs should be lighted so that each step, particularly the step edges, can be clearly seen while going up and down stairs. The lighting should not produce glare or shadows along the stairway.

❐ Use the maximum wattage bulb allowed by the light fixture. (If you do not know the correct wattage, use a bulb no larger than 60 watts.)

❐ Reduce glare by using frosted bulbs, indirect lighting, shades or globes on light fixtures, or partially closing blinds and curtains.

❐ Have a qualified person add additional light fixtures. Make sure that the bulbs you use are the right type and wattage for the light fixture.

QUESTION: Are light switches located at both the top and bottom of the stairs.

RECOMMENDATION: Even if you are very familiar with the

stairs, lighting is an important factor in preventing falls. You should be able to turn on the lights before you use the stairway from either end.

☐ If no other light is available, keep an operating flashlight in a convenient location at the top and bottom of the stairs.

☐ Install night lights at nearby outlets.

☐ Consider installing switches at the top and bottom of the stairs.

QUESTION: Do the steps allow secure footing?

____YES ____NO

RECOMMENDATION: Worn treads or worn or loose carpeting can lead to insecure footing, resulting in slips or falls.

☐ Try to avoid wearing only socks or smooth-soled shoes or slippers when using stairs.

☐ Make certain the carpet is firmly attached to the steps all along the stairs.

☐ Consider refinishing or replacing worn treads, or replacing worn carpeting.

☐ Paint outside steps with paint that has a rough texture, or use abrasive strips.

QUESTION: Are steps even and of the same size and height?

____YES ____NO

RECOMMENDATION: Even a small difference in step surfaces or riser heights can lead to falls.

☐ Mark any steps which are especially narrow or have risers that are higher or lower than the others. Be especially careful of these steps when using the stairs.

QUESTION: Are the coverings on the steps in good condition?

____YES ____NO

RECOMMENDATION: Worn or torn coverings or nails sticking out from coverings could snag your foot or cause you to trip.

❐   Repair coverings.

❐   Remove coverings.

❐   Replace coverings.

QUESTION: Can you clearly see the edges of the steps?

____YES   ____NO

RECOMMENDATION: Falls may occur if the edges of the steps are blurred or hard to see.

❐   Paint edges of outdoor steps white to see them better at night.

❐   Add extra lighting.

❐   If you plan to carpet your stairs, avoid deep pile carpeting or patterned or dark colored carpeting that can make it difficult to see the edges of the steps clearly.

QUESTION: Is anything stored on the stairway, even temporarily?

____YES   ____NO

RECOMMENDATION: People can trip over objects left on stairs, particularly in the event of an emergency or fire.

Remove all objects from the stairway.

REMEMBER,
PERIODICALLY RE-CHECK
YOUR HOME!

From left, front row: Mama Jus, Cherise Dyke, Tom Dyke,
Casey Jo Dyke
Back row: Frank Dyke, René Dyke, and Patricia Dyke,
1975

Chapter 4:

My Experiences as an In-Home Eldercare Provider

After Mama Jus had lived in Westminster Manor for approximately five years, I began to notice changes.

Burn marks the length of her cigarettes on the carpet by her favorite TV chair and her tongue's sounding large shortly after 5:00 PM nearly every day was routine. Although I had worked to discourage Mama Jus' habitual smoking and early-evening toddies, she had made friends with the maid service personnel, and tipping made access to cigarettes and alcohol easy. The maids were more than happy to keep their benefactor in cigarettes and vodka.

By this time, her old friends were gone: Margie to Alzheimer's and Lyle to his male friends. I knew Mama Jus was getting lonely, but it was a little alarming to discover that she was having parties with new, invisible friends. I dropped by nearly every day to see her, and one afternoon I arrived to find her breakfast table set for four. Of course I surmised that she was entertaining friends, but I was taken aback when she introduced me to her invisible friends, and whispered to me that it was only cordial to offer them a drink. Since the maids were buying mom vodka and cigarettes—and probably getting nice tips—my attempt at behavior correction was a failure.

> *See InformationResearchPro CD Category:*
> *Alcohol and Smoking*

Where Should Mama Jus Be?

That's when I began to talk seriously with my wife about the situation. At the time we lived in a small house and Mama Jus was living at Westminster Manor, an assisted living facility. The possible solutions were to move Mom to a different assisted living home, a nursing home or to find a house that all of us, especially Mom, could enjoy together.

After a review of all of our relevant financial data—which included Social Security benefits, Medicare, Medigap and the alternative of Long-Term Care for Mama Jus—as well as the assets each of us had, we were confident that we could keep Mama Jus with us.

That meant finding a suitable home, selling our home and Mama Jus' condo, and moving all of us into the new place.

After much discussion with my wife and Mama Jus, we started looking for a home with a floor plan suitable for all of us. The homes on the market that were ready to go were too expensive, so we found a potentially perfect "fixer-upper."

It was in a quiet neighborhood where Mom could go for walks along the street safely. There would be enough space for Mom to entertain her friends (real friends, not just the imaginary ones), and it was workable financially for all of us.

Mom's room had its own bathroom and was separated from the rest of the bedrooms with easy access to the kitchen and living areas as well as a second front door for her.

We bought the house and began remodeling immediately. Mom picked her colors for the walls and trim, and the carpet for her room. Her bedroom had enough room for the bed she had used for years, her vanity and chest-of-drawers—all familiar objects to her. We added a large planter-box window in which she could grow plants and flowers of her own choosing. Mom was happy with getting to provide so much input. I guess she remembered back when Dad had made all of the decisions, and now she felt she was being treated equally. She was as much a part of the deal as anyone. Mom was happy.

The lot dropped nearly ten feet from one side to the other and more than that from front to back. It had large oaks, a zoysia grass lawn, a large partially covered deck in the back suitable for entertaining, and generous rooms to accommodate all three of us.

We updated the kitchen, rebuilt the fireplace, replaced the floor coverings with wood, and painted inside and out. All of the light fixtures were replaced, the baths were updated, and the yard was landscaped with beautiful plants in newly constructed beds and finished with limestone walkways.

I supervised the entire project, and was elated to have played such an active role in preparing a home in which Mama Jus would live out her life with us. I got this part right.

See InformationResearchPro CD Category: Home Safety Check List.

We completed our plan by selling our house and Mom's condo, and moving into our newly remodeled home.

Our new home was great, but preparing for the challenges of caregiving had escaped me completely. I realized day-by-day that I was not prepared, and the learning curve kept rising. What Mrs. Johnson, had told me, "Get ready for a serious and extended adjustment period," came into sharp focus. If I had educated myself about and prepared myself for what was coming and what caring for an elderly parent demanded, I would have done a better job for all of us. The range of emotions, the time demands and the work was overwhelming until I learned to cope. *I was not prepared!*

See InformationResearchPro CD Categories: Caregiver, Caregiving, Eldercare, Eldercare Blogs, and Emotions

All went exceptionally well until the day of Mama Jus' first party for her friends. Mom told me she would like to have several of her friends from Westminster Manor and one old friend from Houston over for lunch. I thought it was a great idea and I let it go at that. A few days later I asked Mom when her friends were coming for lunch and she told me, "This Friday." That was just three days away, but you know, she was my mom and I knew she could take care of a luncheon for a half-dozen of her friends just like she had in the past. I was sure she had called all of them the day she mentioned the luncheon, and that she had planned her meal. I didn't want to interfere, and especially I wanted her to enjoy her independence. And, of course, I assumed she had made arrangements for the meal. That was my first big mistake—Mama Jus was slipping and I didn't realize it (or I didn't want to realize it).

Friday morning came, and I asked Mom what I could do to help prepare for the luncheon. She said, "Nothing, they aren't coming." I asked what had happened, and she replied, "No one could come. They all had something else to do, and it was just a bad idea." I said, "Mom, when did you call them?" She replied, "Yesterday afternoon." I said, "Mom, do you think you gave them enough notice?" She said, "I think they just didn't want to come."

She never mentioned having her friends over for anything again.

I hadn't realized what was happening to Mom. Since she moved to Austin, she almost never planned anything in advance. Around the Manor, most events were spur-of-the-moment or they were listed on the bulletin board for all to see (with plenty of notice).

Naturally, she didn't think any of her friends would have had anything to do, so a few hours' notice was plenty. Much as a youngster doesn't give any thought to what it takes to plan a party, including notice to the prospective guests, Mama Jus no longer did either. I should have anticipated what might happen, but I didn't. So, the great place we prepared for Mom to entertain her friends was never used by her that way—what a mistake. It was my first mistake, and it was a harbinger of what was to come.

Looking back, I guess that I was not willing to accept that Mama Jus was slipping and she would be needing a little help and care with a lot of things immediately, and a lot of help with most things at some point. Already I knew that I was not prepared to give Mama Jus the care that she would need.

Bank Accounts and Banking

When Mama Jus moved in we discussed her bank account and her Social Security benefits. She was still thinking clearly, and she understood why she should have another name on her bank account and why her Social Security check should be direct deposited into her bank account.

Before we changed her bank account and directed the government to direct deposit her Social Security check into her account, I talked to my brother about it. It is important to keep such dealings up front and out in the open for all to see.

Joint accounts and multiple signatures are a good idea. Both for legal and practical reasons, have multiple (at least two) signatories per account. That way, you can bank for your elder and withdraw funds upon their demise. But, be sure to keep everyone advised of the arrangement. It helps prevent hard feelings and suspicions when the time comes.

See InformationResearchPro CD Category: Asset Management and Banking

Incontinence

At some point in time it became apparent that Mama Jus was experiencing incontinence. She was reticent to admit it, but finally she admitted that she was having a "little leakage." My wife came to the rescue— she suggested that we get Mama Jus adult diapers to try. That seemed easy enough to me, and I went to the drugstore and bought a bundle of adult diapers. To my dismay, there were a number of choices. So, I chose a brand and brought them home for Mama Jus to use.

I should have known that adult diapers are not all alike. They are just like clothing: suits, blouses, underwear and the like. Each manufacturer has its own style and cut, and they are not the same from brand to brand. And brands have different sizes and styles within their brand name. There is more to selecting an adult diaper than just picking a brand randomly.

So, even though I thought I had solved Mama Jus' problem, I was wrong. Mom complained that she had a little leakage—she was not referring to incontinence, she was referring to leakage around her legs. So, I went back to the drugstore and bought another brand. How stupid! I was now involved in a hit-or-miss program in selecting adult diapers for my mother. My second choice (and second trip to the drugstore) seemed to do the trick.

Oops, I just thought I had solved the problem. I soon noticed that Mama Jus' bed had the faint odor of urine. Gently, I asked her if she had wet her bed, and she replied in her soft and innocent voice, "No, I don't think so." My routine was to wash her sheets twice a week unless I smelled the odor. Soon, it seemed that the odor was present every day. What was the problem?

One morning I noticed that Mama Jus was washing her stomach as soon as she got out of bed. I inquired why she was washing her stomach and she told me that her stomach was "moist."

You guessed it. Now Mama Jus' diapers seemed to be leaking around the waist band. Normally gravity takes any leakage down, and if the leg elastics hold secure, there is no leakage. But when Mama Jus started wearing her diapers to bed, the urine went in all directions. And, if the waistband was not tight every inch of the way around, out it came.

So, I went back to the drugstore(s) and chose two more brands in her size. Fortunately, one of them was a perfect fit and almost all leakage stopped. Note that I said "almost all." In the final analysis, I chose an adult diaper that minimized the leakage, and resigned myself to washing Mama Jus' sheets every day.

What I should have done to choose an adult diaper for Mama Jus was to be methodical and thorough. I should have bought several brands and sizes the first time around, and had a "fitting." I should have known that moisture can go in all directions, and have made sure that the fit was good both at the legs and the waist. In short, I should have given it more time and attention. I did not know it then, but I do now. And so do you!

> *See InformationResearchPro CD Category:*
> *Incontinence*

Diapers take more room than underwear. So clothes that once fit perfectly may fit too snuggly when worn over diapers. Make sure the clothes fit loosely enough for your loved one to get into and out of them easily. If not, the diapers will not get changed as often and sometimes will not get worn at all. You know what that means.

Sometimes they forget (or choose not to remember), so check them often.

Remember, your charge is not an eight- to twenty-pound baby, but a 100-plus-pound adult. So when you help them clean up after soiling their diaper, check all the way up the fanny crease to ensure your loved one is kept clean.

Before we leave the topic of incontinence, I have one more thing to cover. Just like me, you will soon discover that the mattress is also in harm's way. But it's impossible to wash a mattress. What I was late to discover about the diapers affected the mattress, too. I tried cleaning the mattress and airing it in the sun, but that was not a workable solution. Before I understood the leakage problem, the mattress was ruined. I was not thinking that Mama Jus might wet the bed indirectly. Think through everything that happens, and where it can lead; a little analysis will go a long way toward prevention of the "next step" in the chain of events. Anything can and will happen, if you don't think it through and take precautions.

My wife knew just what to do. She guided me to the bedding store to get an impervious mattress pad (at least two of them) for Mama Jus' bed. We (ha!), my wife, made sure that the pad had elastic straps at all corners to secure the pad to the bed, so it couldn't slip out of place. Finally, a system was in place from the right diapers to a mattress cover.

> *See InformationResearchPro CD Category:*
> *Incontinence*

As a part of our remodeling to make ready for Mama Jus, we installed the carpet of her choice in her bedroom. It was a nice neutral-colored Berber with a generous carpet pad. The plan was to use carpet so her floor would not be cold in the winter months. All of us thought the flooring choice was a great idea, but we discovered about two years or so later that we had made a mistake. The flooring should have been something impervious to everything. Although we had the carpet treated with Scotchgard, that protector goes only so far. Leaks finally overcome the Scotchgard, and then it's up to ChemDry or a service like it to clean the carpet.

Mama Jus awoke one morning and had a bout of diarrhea. For some reason she had tried to undo her diaper before she got out of bed, and as she headed for the bathroom…you know what happened. There were spots on the carpet from her bed all the way into the bathroom. After an urgent carpet cleaning by ChemDry, we resolved to go to Plan B. We bought flexible (but tough) plastic runners that have pointed grippers on the underside to keep the runners from slipping. (Realtors use the runners over carpet when they hold an Open House.) I placed the runners over the carpet along both sides as well as the footboard end of Mama Jus' bed and on to the bathroom. That did the job.

Although all of us had the best intentions when we selected Mama Jus' carpet, we did not plan far enough ahead. We should have chosen either a wood laminate or a nice vinyl. We would have avoided the multiple carpet-cleaning expenses, and the wood laminate or vinyl would have been much more serviceable.

See InformationResearchPro CD Categories: Incontinence, Bowel Dysfunction

I am relieved to report that Mama Jus had no real bowel dysfunction other than an occasional bout of diarrhea. Your loved one may experience bowel dysfunction, so I make reference to the subject here and call your attention to the category on the CD.

See InformationResearchPro CD Category:
Bowel Dysfunction

Supervision, Safety, and Security

When Mama Jus first moved in my goal was to make sure she had as much independence as possible. Complete freedom was great at first, but as time passed and the normal aging process began to work on her body and her mind, I had to start exercising more supervision and control to keep her safe and sound.

Initially, Mama Jus had keys to the doors and could go outside and walk or enjoy the yard and the back deck as she pleased. She could and did answer the door when the bell rang as well as answer the telephone on occasion.

Some two years or so after Mama Jus moved in she went missing. I searched the house, the porches, the back deck, and the yard, but no Mama Jus. It was just like realizing that one of our grandchildren was missing. With each passing minute, concern and near-panic washes over you, and you get busy looking intently while trying to fight off all sorts of fears that pop into your mind.

I ran to the street and looked up and down the block. Then I went to both ends of the block to check the side streets—still no Mama Jus. Then I decided to go all the way around the block, and by this time I was running. To my great relief I found Mama Jus sitting on the curb all the way around the block at its lowest point—about thirty feet lower than the street in front of our home.

As I approached and asked if she were OK, she smiled and told me that she was just resting. She told me that she couldn't get up the hill in either direction. She had tried, but she was not strong enough to climb the steepness of the road. It wasn't very steep, but it was enough to stop her old legs from pulling the grade. I told her to wait right there, and I would go get the car and drive her home. All is well that ends well, but darn, it was a tense few minutes. And both of us realized that her old body was not as strong as it once was.

I had to start taking precautions not to let her over extend her diminishing physical abilities. It sounds easy and straight forward, but Mama Jus' judgment entered the equation, too. I had to decide whether she had the judgment to know what she could do and what she couldn't do, or what she should do and what she shouldn't do in her "new" physical state. That proved to be more difficult than just gauging her physical abilities.

See InformationResearchPro CD Category: Exercise

Just a few months later I was working in the back-yard, Sibyl was working at her office in Tarrytown, and Mama Jus was in the house. I stopped what I was doing to cool off and get a drink of water. I walked into the house to get a water bottle and to my surprise found Mama Jus sitting in the den talking to a young man I did not know—a stranger alone in the house with Mom. When I inquired who he was and what he was doing in the house, he sheepishly replied, "I sell magazines and rang the doorbell. The nice lady answered the door and invited me in." I couldn't blame him, too much, but I was realizing more and more that Mom's judgment was becoming an issue. What if neither Sib nor I had been at home? What if the young man was unscrupulous and had helped himself to silverware or objects-of-art, or worse? I had to take action to make the house more secure—from the inside. This included purchasing security products that sound an alarm when doors open or close, and that give recorded reminders and warnings.

See InformationResearchPro CD Category:
Safety

Mama Jus really enjoyed the back deck. Much of it was covered. It had a large ceiling fan and comfortable outdoor furniture. It was a story above the back yard, so sitting on the deck put you "up in the big oak trees" with the birds and squirrels. She just loved it back there.

Unfortunately, the French doors that opened onto the deck had both handle locks and keyed deadbolts. The deadbolts caused no problems for Mama Jus, but the little handle locks that work with the twist of your fingers were a problem for her. Depending on whether the handle locks were locked or not, the deck-side part of the handle could be disengaged. If it were turned the "wrong" way as Mama Jus went out to enjoy the deck, the handle would not engage the keeper and she was locked out of the house. (I must confess that it happened to me more than once, but I could go down the steep steps to the backyard, walk up the driveway and then the steps up to the front door.)

As time passed, Mama Jus' getting locked out of the house became more frequent. After a number of times, she quit using the deck. For her, that left using the front doors her only acceptable option to getting outside, and that put her on the front porch with access to the street. Now what?

The front doorknobs did not have the same locking mechanism as the French doors to the deck, so Mama Jus did not have a problem getting in and out the front doors. But, with access to the front porch, she could go anywhere and let anyone into the house. I had to find a solution to the security challenge.

While browsing in a large hardware store I was approached by one of the floor salesman. I described my problem about security, and he said he had just the product. It was a baby-proofing hollow-knob attachment that fits loosely over the actual doorknob and snaps together. If your hand is *not* large enough and strong enough to squeeze the outer shell against the knob and turn it, you cannot open the door. That seemed simple enough, and I couldn't get home quickly enough to give it a try.

After putting the shells over the knobs and figuring out how to snap them into place, I found that it was not as easy to work as represented. We used them for nearly two years, but our guests (and us at times) couldn't make them work quickly and easily. Oh well, it was the best solution I could find, so we used them anyway. At least that stopped Mama Jus from going out or letting strangers into the house.

> *See InformationResearchPro CD Category:*
> *Products (Many security products are available such as*
> *latches, alarms, secure knobs and automatic recorded*
> *messages and warnings.)*

At some point in time you realize that your elderly parent's behavior has reverted to that of a child. It happens slowly or least it did for us, but at some point an event brings it into sharp focus.

One afternoon I was cleaning out the rain gutters and Sib was off showing property. Mama Jus was in the house puttering around harmlessly when I went outside. After completing my task, I walked into the house and the smell of natural gas was strong. I saw that Mama Jus was in the kitchen going through the drawers as I ran to check the gas cook-top. Sure enough, not one but two of the gas jets were on full blast (no pun intended). I turned them off and quickly opened all of the doors. About that time Mama Jus told me in a frustrated voice that she could not find the matches. Thank goodness the kitchen matches were in the pantry, and it was latched shut.

Sibyl and I preferred a gas oven to an electric oven, so that is what we used. We had not considered that Mama Jus, who was not doing any of the cooking, would ever use it for anything.

I was shaken to say the least, and we redoubled our efforts to guard against such potentially devastating events. As parents we try to protect our children from possible dangers, but their short stature helps us. We put hazardous things "up and out of their reach." But with our elderly parents it's a different story—they can reach just about anything we can. So, we have to take extra care in keeping potentially devastating items out of their reach.

We explained to Mama Jus what might have happened and extracted her promise not to use the gas oven and cook-top. And we repeated our warning and extracted her promise almost daily for two weeks. Finally, when she started reacting to our warnings with noticeable disgust, we were satisfied that she was well aware of the danger. She never attempted to use the gas cook-top again. In hind site, an electric oven might have been the better choice.

Darn that Murphy! You know, that guy who says that if something can go wrong, it will: drop a jelly sandwich and it always lands jelly-side down? Well, the routine we developed with Mama Jus was for her to take a shower every morning as soon as she got out of bed. Her room had a nice tile shower with safety handles and a door mounted on top of a four-inch dam. Just step over the dam and start the shower. It was perfect, and what could go wrong?

I found out that at least two things could (and did) go wrong. To make sure that Mama Jus felt that she was "independent," I left her showering to her—no interference from me. It was an early morning, sometime during Mama Jus' third year with us. I was in the kitchen starting to make breakfast when I heard Mama Jus go into her bathroom.

I then heard the shower start and soon Mama Jus was screaming at the top of her lungs. I ran into her bathroom and found her standing in her shower with HOT water blasting her soft skin. I turned it off before any real damage was done, and asked her what had happened. She said that she got into the shower and just happened to turn the hot water handle on first. Before she could turn on the cold water and adjust the water to her liking, it was very hot and nearly scalding her. Rather than stepping out of her shower, she stood there and screamed. It could have been serious had I not been close enough to hear her screams and take quick action.

I talked with Mom about turning on the water and adjusting the temperature before stepping under the water. Although I think the event impressed her enough to keep her from repeating what happened, I told her I would be privileged if she would let me start her shower for her in the mornings. She smiled and told me that was fine with her—so that's what I did from then on.

Remember this when you set your hot-water tank's temperature setting. It might not be convenient to set it on a lower heat level, but it could protect your loved one from getting scalded.

See InformationResearchPro CD Category: Skin

Not long after that we had another unusual experience related to the morning shower. I had adjusted the water for Mama Jus, she got into the shower and told me it was just right. I told her that I was going to fix her favorite breakfast, two scrambled eggs, toast and strawberry jelly and orange slices, and to call if she needed me.

Usually her showers were brief, so I was wasting no time in getting her breakfast ready. I had her meal ready and on the table, but no Mama Jus. I walked into her room, but no Mama Jus. I started to walk into her bathroom when I stepped on wet carpet, and then into water on the bathroom floor. I opened the shower door and there she was sitting on the shower floor—right on the drain.

I don't know what she hit with her arm when she fell, but it pealed a one-inch strip of skin about two inches down her arm. Other than that she wasn't hurt. Thankfully Neosporin and a soft bandage around her arm saved the skin and it healed in about a week.

As misfortune would have it, she sat on the drain when she fell. It didn't take long for the water to overflow the dam, cover the bathroom floor and start invading her bedroom. From then on I checked on her progress in the shower frequently—each and every morning.

See InformationResearchPro CD Category: Skin

Help From the Family—<u>All</u> of the Family

My wife was a full-time real estate broker when Mama Jus moved in and she maintained her business the entire five-plus years Mama Jus was with us. In addition, my wife was caring for her youngest daughter, Laura, who was diagnosed with juvenile diabetes at age seven.

Laura was about twenty-seven when Mama Jus moved in, and passed away about four years later. Laura lived in her own apartment, but she needed lots of help. Sibyl's hands were full; however, Sibyl helped me with Mama Jus and contributed all she could to make it work.

One might think there would be friction or competition between two adult women in the same house, but it is not necessarily so. Mama Jus recognized Sibyl as my wife and the lady of the house. So, we never had a problem with scheduling, meal planning, furniture arranging, temperature control (except between my wife and me) and all of the other items that require choice, preference and decisions. A little discretion by all of us made it work. We discussed this at the onset of our arrangement and agreed that we would make it work—and it did.

When Sibyl and I married we joined families. She had two girls and two boys and I had two boys. Five of our six children lived in Austin, and they dropped in to see Mama Jus from time to time. It was a real joy to me to see her eyes light up when they arrived. She wanted to feed them and give them as much attention as she could. I know it was happy and healthy for both generations, and I will always be grateful to our children for the time they spent with my Mama Jus.

Regardless of the circumstance, *the rest of the immediately-related family must help the primary caregiver.* And if they do not do it voluntarily, use all means available to make them participate. Shame them, beg them, and reason with them. Do what it takes to get them involved. And do it early.

What they need to realize is you are carrying a heavy load. In essence, you are caring for a one hundred- to two hundred-pound child who can put an adult-sized load in their diaper. And when the time comes, you will be helping your loved one change a diaper several times a day as well as all of the other many and endless duties of care giving. And, it's constant. So, any help you get is a blessing to both you and your loved one.

For instance, you will be bathing, feeding, dressing, entertaining and helping in and out of chairs and bed and doors and stairs and cars and on and on...It will take most of your time and attention and your relatives need to know what the job demands. So tell them that you do what you do gladly, but you need all the help they can give you.

Unfortunately, Mama Jus' other living son and grandchildren, other than my boys, lived in Houston, Florida and California—a long way from Austin, Texas. However, my brother invited Mama Jus down to Florida for two to three weeks each summer and gave me the chance to take a break. She would spend two or three weeks down there visiting with Dave, his wife and their teenage daughter. It was a welcomed relief, and it let him know first-hand what care giving for our elderly parent entailed day in and day out.

How did the travel work? First, we made arrangements in advance with the departing airline to have a wheelchair waiting for her at the curbside.

Second, a nice tip to the porter at curbside assured great service all the way through the airport and to the boarding gate. The airline agent took over from there and got Mama Jus to her seat on the plane. On the return trip, Dave used the same largess to get Mama Jus safely back to us.

At either end of Mama Jus' trip, as soon as Dave or I had Mama Jus in custody, we would get her into the car with my wife or his wife and then go back in the airport to get her luggage. It worked well every year.

Since we had no one else who had the ability and desire to keep Mama Jus for two or three weeks, we planned our vacation around her trips to Florida.

Mama Jus' granddaughters who lived in Houston invited her down for Thanksgiving dinner once or twice. That helped, too. It was a pleasant respite for both of us.

Watch your loved one's eyes light up when small children and babies come into the home. Whether the neighbors' or the extended family's little ones, encourage their parents to being them to see your loved one as frequently as possible. They are "what the doctor ordered" and double doses are great. When my boys or my wife's children or my brothers' children brought their children by to see Mama Jus, her eyes lit up, a smile came to her face and she exalted in their presence. She reveled in their company. And she always asked them to come back soon. The effects usually lasted for several days, too.

Earlier, I mentioned that Mama Jus enjoyed smoking and having a drink in the late afternoon.

Habits are hard to break—especially for the one who has to break them. But there is a substantial involvement, emotionally and otherwise, for those helping them, too. Mama Jus had two habits that were not good for her health. They affected those around her, and set a poor example for the youngsters.

Both Frank and Mama Jus smoked since I could remember. From time to time Frank would give up his cigarettes, but Mama Jus never made the effort. She like to smoke and that was that.

After Frank died and Mama Jus moved to Austin, she began having more than one drink in the evenings. I didn't like it, but I accepted the commonly-used rationalization for both her drinking and smoking, "At her age what difference does it make? Let her enjoy her final years without a fuss."

Eventually, though, I noticed the burn marks on the carpet, mentioned earlier, and it was her drinking and smoking that prompted me to think about moving her into our home. I didn't want to risk her falling and injuring herself or her setting her apartment on fire and our losing her.

My rationalizations about her drinking and smoking in her final years were no longer rational. It had to stop, and I was the only one who was in a position to encourage and enforce a change in her behavior. After we moved Mama Jus in with us, it took about a year to "wean" her from smoking and her evening drink.

> *See InformationResearchPro CD Category:*
> *Alcohol, Smoking*

From time to time Mama Jus would tell me that she sure would like to have a cigarette but, when reminded as to what the doctor had told us about smoking and the possible results, she would let it drop. Neither my wife nor I drank, other than occasionally, so she was not tempted in that regard either. It all went very well—at least until she would go to visit my brother in Florida or her grandchildren in Houston.

Mama Jus made four trips during the last five years of her life to visit her Dave in Florida or her granddaughters in Houston. One day I received a telephone call from one of the granddaughters. She told me they had finished Thanksgiving dinner, during which Mama Jus had had several glasses of wine. She tripped getting up from the table, fell and broke her wrist.

I was also informed by my brother that his family in Florida let Mom smoke whenever she pleased "She just has a few years left, so what's it gonna hurt?"

I am sure that both my brother and Mama Jus' grandchildren had the best intentions and all of them made the same convenient rationalization that I made early on—"Heck, she's in her last years so what will a drink and a cigarette hurt." What they did not appreciate was what it took for both Mama Jus and me to break her habits the first time and why. And old habits come roaring back without much encouragement. Consequently, every time Mama Jus returned from a trip, we would have to break the habits again.

Let your relatives know that one little drink *will* hurt, and one cigarette *will* hurt, because it takes a long time to get those old habits back in the box. More requests and demands and arguments, more refusals and telling Mom *no*—it's not fun. And, that one little drink leds to sneaking sips (gulps) out of the bottle when no one was looking and the sad result. Mama Jus, who had a very low tolerance for alcohol, became buzzed quickly and then fell and broke her wrist. Fortunately for the well-intending relative it was a short-lived incident, but then Mama Jus returned home to recover and rehab—weeks of extra attention and trips to the doctor and the rehab clinic.

Do not be hesitant about informing your relatives about the habits that you have helped your loved one change. Regardless of the behavior that you have worked to change with *your* "Mama Jus," be clear and direct with relatives about your unique set of facts, and remind them that you do not want to have to plow the same ground again.

See InformationResearchPro CD Categories:
Alcohol and Smoking

Mama Jus' Insatiable Appetite

Mama Jus was never a grazer. She was never overweight. She ate small portions and chewed every bite fifty times—at least. That was something that was drummed into her head as a young girl. That was a good thing, and she enjoyed good health and a trim figure nearly all of her life—nearly all of her life.

About the third year after she moved into our home, I noticed that she was snacking incessantly. At first, I did not think anything of it, but when her clothes started getting a little snug I began to wonder. Leftovers were disappearing, and crumbs were showing up on the kitchen counters and around Mama Jus' bed. When we began to notice dirty silverware and dishes in the sink, it dawned on us that Mama Jus was eating five or six times a day in *addition* to the three-square meals we prepared for her.

One morning, maybe fifteen minutes after she had finished a breakfast of two eggs, whole wheat toast with strawberry jam and orange slices, she asked if I was trying to starve her. I thought she was teasing me after the healthful breakfast I had fed her but, when she accused me again of trying to starve her, I started asking questions.

First, I asked if she was kidding, and she replied no. She was serious. Then I asked if she had enjoyed the scrambled eggs and toast with her favorite jam, and she asked, "What are you talking about?" Then I showed her the dirty dishes, and reminded her that she had watched me peel the orange for her. She gave me a blank look and returned to her bedroom.

I was stumped and asked Sibyl what she thought was happening. She reminded me that she wondered if Mama Jus was having mini-strokes from time-to-time and pointed out that a little stroke might have affected the part of her brain that signals when one is hungry and when one is sated.

Although I accepted Sib's explanation, I wanted to make sure. I called Dr. Pete, our good friend and neurologist. He confirmed the possibility Sib had suggested, but advised me to bring Mama Jus in for a checkup. Shortly thereafter Mama Jus was sitting before Dr. Pete who, after a few tests and a lengthy visit, determined that in fact Mama Jus had experienced mini-strokes which had affected the part of her brain that signals hunger and satiation.

Not much later began a series of rather bizarre incidents. Without Dr. Pete's diagnosis, these occurrences would have been hard to understand.

One afternoon I came into the kitchen. On top of the table was a sack of dog food, with Mama Jus sitting in a chair next to it. That wasn't too strange until I noticed that she had crumbs all around her mouth—dog food crumbs. I asked her if she was hungry, but she told me no. She said that she had just had a snack, and pointed to the sack of dog food. "It was good, too."

Next I found Mama Jus eating directly from the mayonnaise and the peanut butter jars, using a long-handled iced-tea spoon to access the very last bit. A shorter spoon, also used, was lying on the table.

The final straw was finding Mama Jus pulling stuffing out of a turkey breast. Thanksgiving leftovers are great, and I like them, too. But, she was reaching into the cavity with her hand and grabbing all she could— no spoon, no fork, just her hand. Something had to be done.

Mama Jus was eating all the time. So, because of her constant hunger, her tight fitting clothes and what Dr. Pete told us, I knew that I had to take action. But what could I do? What *should* I do?

After discussing the problem with Sibyl, we agreed that we needed to put locks on the refrigerator and the pantry—easier said than done. A lock for Mama Jus is a lock for Tom and Sibyl, too. Having a lock on the refrigerator and the pantry was probably not a bad idea for all of us, but can you imagine?

I found locks for both and tried them out, but it was just too much. You don't realize how many times a day you need access to things in the kitchen. It's not just food items that are stored in the pantry—it's all sorts of stuff. So, mechanical locks were not the answer. Instead, I used long kitchen towels that could be knotted and unknotted quickly. In fact, once Mama Jus could see the towel tied on the refrigerator doors she gave up. After a time, I could just wrap the towel around the handles and she never discovered my deception.

I put a small hook latch on the pantry door above Mama Jus' reach, and that did that. It may seem cruel, but it was either that or give her free access to whatever she wanted to eat, whenever she wanted to eat. The inevitable results would have been obesity, high blood pressure, or worse, as well as clothes that no longer fit and possibly unsanitary conditions for us all.

In summary, I learned that the brain offers many targets for mini-strokes, and her eating disorder was the result of a direct hit to one of them. According to the neurologist, a mini-clot had affected the area of her brain that signaled when her stomach was full. Mama Jus' constant hunger overwhelmed her short-term memory, so she was *always* hungry.

Those great TV ads for food do not help either. It must be torture for one who truly thinks they aren't being fed. It takes some vigilance, but it helps to shield that "hungry" loved one from those delicious TV ads.

Secretary / Bill Payer

Mama Jus had a few bills, bank statements, AARP literature and a number of solicitations that she wanted to service. When we noticed that she was 'slipping' with addresses, stamps, and timing, I talked with Mama Jus about what was happening as gently as I could. Fortunately, a friend who was caring for an elderly parent told me about a secretary/bill-paying service that they used. The service provider came by their home every two weeks and took care of the bills, the statements and any extra items for a very moderate fee.

It was a great idea and it worked great for us, too. Mama Jus had a new "friend" who spent time with her exclusively, paid her bills, balanced her check book and took care of those extra items. For Mama Jus, the extras were completing those solicitations that involved "sweepstakes" with intricate forms and huge winning prizes and visiting about her potential winnings. In fact, the prizes offered were often a million dollars or more. Although the odds of winning were one in fifty million, Mama Jus wanted those entries completed and mailed so she would have something to leave to her grandchildren.

Completing those detailed forms drove me crazy, but her new personal assistant didn't mind it a bit. It was a win-win-win. Mama Jus maintained some of her independence and had a new confidant. I avoided busy-work I didn't have time to do and the personal assistant earned a nominal fee for her service.

Outside Care Providers

We were well into the fifth year with Mama Jus. Unless she went to visit with my brother or her grandchildren, I had full charge of Mama Jus. It was hard to leave the house to do anything without taking her with me or securing her in the house, and it made taking care of business almost impossible. It was much like watching a young child—it was demanding and required constant attention. I had to have some relief.

When Mama Jus came home from Houston that Thanksgiving with a broken right wrist (she was right-handed), the added time and attention demanded just about drove me over the edge. I contacted an agency that provided on-site eldercare, and contracted for a young Licensed Vocational Nurse (LVN) to spend several hours several times a week with Mama Jus. The young LVN could help Mom with the therapy, drive her to and from the clinic and give me a little relief. It was almost heavenly to have a little free time—free time that I had not had for nearly five years.

The LVN hadn't been with us for long when I noticed Mama Jus on the front porch smoking a cigarette. Where did she get the cigarettes... and the matches? When I asked her where she got the cigarette, she told me it was in her drawer. After she reluctantly extinguished her smoke, I asked her to show me where she got the cigarette.

I followed her inside to her bedroom where she pointed to one of her vanity drawers. I opened it and there was a nearly full pack of cigarettes and a small box of matches. For some reason I checked the next drawer down and there was a carton of cigarettes less one pack and a whole package of match boxes.

That led me to my next question: How did the cigarettes and matches get there? She hated to tell me, but she finally confessed to convincing the LVN to get them for her. In spite of my pressure, she would not tell me how she paid for the contraband—she said that she didn't remember. How could I argue with that?

The next time the LVN arrived I asked her about the cigarettes. I got the same answer that Mama Jus' relatives had given me before—"She doesn't have many years left so what's wrong with letting her have her cigarettes?"

Not telling me before she made her unilateral decision to get Mama Jus cigarettes and matches was a little odd to say the least. And she, the LVN, got defensive when I started pressing for more information: Who paid for them, why didn't she consult me, etc. The LVN told me that she had paid for them because she felt sorry for Mama Jus. That was more than a little suspicious to me, and that was the last day for the LVN.

It wasn't a day or two later that Sibyl noticed that Mama Jus was not wearing her watch—a fine watch that my dad had given her years ago. It no longer worked, but it was a fine watch with a platinum band. I think Mama Jus wore it for sentimental reasons, and she wore it every day.

Because of the timing, we took the liberty of looking through Mama Jus' jewelry box. Sibyl noticed that several items were missing, and we guessed that might explain the LVN's generous purchase of the cigarettes and matches for Mama Jus. I apologize for my conclusions if I am wrong, but the timing and the LVN's explanation suggested that she left with the best of the bargain.

It might have been that Mama Jus just gave her "new friend" some nice jewelry and that was that. Regardless, as a precaution, *always* keep your and your loved one's valuables under lock and key, and *control the key*.

After having the LVN around to watch Mama Jus, take her to the store and for rides in her car, I was getting spoiled. I liked having a little time to myself, and I wasn't ready to go back to devoting 100% of my time to caring for my mom. Shame on me!

About the time we gave up the LVN, a friend of ours told us about a caregiver their family had used for nearly seven years. She was big and strong and really good with their dad. He had passed away a few months before, so she was available. She had provided in-home care and had moved their dad into her home off and on for his last two years. It had worked well for everyone, and our friend gave her high marks.

That was all I needed. Within a week our new health-care prospect (Ethel) was in our home for a visit. It lasted nearly three hours and included Mama Jus. This time there were lots of questions both ways. We discussed Mama Jus' desire to smoke and have a drink, her eating disorder, her general mental and physical health, and a host of other questions many of which were asked by Ethel. Ethel volunteered that her home was "outfitted" for caring for the elderly, and invited us to inspect it at any time we liked.

After several days and a few more visits by phone, I made the decision to hire Ethel for four hours a day, four days a week. That would give me time to work on a project as well as a little time to myself.

Ethel had a car, so transportation was not a problem. In fact, she would take Mom for drives and to the mall. By that time we were using a wheelchair for Mama Jus when we took her out of the house. She enjoyed being wheeled through the mall and looking at things. It was a welcomed change.

Our new arrangement rocked along without incident for about three months. Mama Jus liked Ethel and Ethel liked Mama Jus. It could not have gone better.

One day, Ethel reminded us that we had not "inspected" her home and asked us to come and look it over. The next day we loaded up Mama Jus and went to visit Ethel at her home. It was as neat as a pin and as clean as a whistle. The front room had a projection TV that Ethel said was purchased two years before by her previous client. He liked to watch movies and sports, so he bought the thing—it was large! Mama Jus seemed enthralled with the giant TV, and when Ethel introduced Mama Jus to "her *new bedroom*," Mama Jus smiled and seemed pleased with the attention she was getting from Ethel. *Hmm…*

It wasn't long before Ethel invited Mama Jus to spend the weekend. To my amazement, Mama Jus said she would like to go.

Ethel took Mama Jus home with her on a Friday afternoon and brought her home Monday morning. Ethel told me Mama Jus had asked for a cigarette, but remembering our initial discussion about Mama Jus' weaknesses, she gently refused her. And that was that. Ethel said she didn't ask again. Maybe she remembered the time when as a young girl she had asked her father for a nickel to get a Coke with her friends and he refused her. She never asked Ethel for another cigarette either.

After a couple of more over-nights that went very well, and another invitation from Ethel for Mama Jus to move in with her on a trial basis, I relented. I had mixed emotions, but I relented nonetheless.

Bedsores: Part 1

I dropped in unannounced a number of days just to see how things were going during the first three weeks of Mama Jus' stay with Ethel. Several times no one was at Ethel's house—they were out and about. But usually, I found Mama Jus there ensconced on the couch watching the giant TV with the controller nearby. The house was always neat and clean, Mama Jus' bed was made, the bathroom and the kitchen sink were clean, and there were no untoward odors.

I must admit I was enjoying my relief from constant care giving and all of the emotions that go with it, but not having Mama Jus under my wing bothered me. Was I defeating my initial goal of having her in our home so I could give her loving care directly, or not? My internal battle continued almost daily.

At the end of Mama Jus' sixth week at Ethel's house, I received a call from Ethel. She told me that Mama Jus had developed a little bedsore, so she needed the name of Mama Jus' doctor and her insurance cards.

I had heard of bedsores, but that is about it. I gave Ethel the name and address of Mama Jus' doctor, but told her that I would make the arrangements, and come and get Mama Jus. Ethel downplayed the bedsore, and assured me that she would drive Mama Jus to the doctor's office and meet me there.

When I called for a doctor's appointment and gave my reason, the receptionist put me on hold. When she came back on the line, she told me that the doctor wanted to see Mama Jus immediately, and scheduled her for nine o'clock the next morning. I was a bit surprised that Mama Jus' appointment was so immediate, but I would soon find out why.

I called Ethel back and gave her the time and location for the appointment. We met at the doctor's office.

I helped Mama Jus into the examining room and waited for the doctor to show. The doctor came in, said hello and took Mama Jus into an examining room. Shortly later, the doctor came out and invited me into the examining room.

She asked if I knew anything about bedsores, and my answer was "very little." Then she asked if I wanted to see them and talk about the prognosis, and of course my answer was yes.

The doctor had already cleaned them, but was waiting to dress and bandage them until I had a chance to see the bedsores first hand. Mama Jus had not one, but two bedsores—one small and the other much larger. The doctor explained that some people are more susceptible to them than others, and that the primary cause, in Mama Jus' case, is sustained pressure on a particular area of the buttocks.

When asked for more detail, the doctor told me that sitting or lying in one spot for prolonged periods of time without movement is the primary cause, i.e. sitting while watching TV or lying in bed can cause the sores. The prolonged pressure on an area restricts the blood flow and the skin will break and start the process that works ever deeper into the tissue if not discovered and checked.

She continued that the skin of the elderly is susceptible to bedsores and there are a number of possible contributing factors. And, the sores are hard to treat and the healing process is usually slow.

One of the sores was fairly pronounced, and the doctor recommended that I take Mama Jus to a surgeon for an examination. Her referral was to Dr. Victor Li-Pelaez, a plastic surgeon whose specialty was treating bedsores.

Rightly or wrongly, I took Mama Jus home with me. After my discussion with the doctor about bedsores, I thought I might have prevented Mama Jus' problem. I now know that you can both see them forming and smell them once they have progressed.

Since part of my routine in caring for Mama Jus was to supervise her morning showers, and to help her dress and undress, as needed, I felt sure that I would have noticed any spots forming on her buttocks. Had I failed my sweet Mama Jus? The old adage "hind site is twenty-twenty" didn't give me much solace, and it still doesn't. I know that I could have prevented the problem had I kept Mama Jus at home with me.

See InformationResearchPro CD Category: Bedsores

Bedsores: Part 2

As soon as we returned home from the doctor's office, I called Dr. Li-Pelaez's office to make an appointment. After telling the doctor's scheduler that Mama Jus' doctor had made the referral and a bit about Mama Jus' problem, an appointment was made for the next day— she said that they would "fit Mama Jus in."

The next morning we didn't have to wait long before Mama Jus was called back to an examining room.

Shortly later Dr. Li-Pelaez walked in with a big smile on his face and introduced himself to Mom and me. His manner could not have been gentler, and I doubt he could have been more thorough. When he concluded his exam, he explained bedsores, in general, and Mama Jus' case specifically.

He noted that the deeper sore needed surgery for sure and that he would wait and make a determination on the smaller sore when he saw how it reacted to treatment. Both of them were infected, and he told us he would schedule her surgery for one or both of them as soon as he arrested the infection. He had her committed to the hospital for treatment.

Within a month or so the infection was arrested and Dr. Li-Pelaez scheduled Mama Jus for surgery at St. David's Hospital. Our good doctor reported that the surgery went well, and that he expected Mama Jus to have a full recovery.

On the other hand, the nurses gave me "what's for." They told me it should never have happened. And they were right. If I had kept Mama Jus with me for those few weeks, I doubt it would have happened. I must say the doctors were not nearly as critical of "our" bedsore as her nurses were, but we'll never know what might have happened had I refused to let Mama Jus go with Ethel.

See InformationResearchPro CD Category:
Bedsores

Although Mama Jus came through the surgery and healed well, the ordeal took its toll. I think it was as much her time in the hospital as the surgery and the anesthesia. She never recovered all of her strength.

During Mama Jus' stay in the hospital she developed dysphagia—she could not swallow.

The doctor ordered a feeding tube be inserted through Mama Jus' nose to her stomach. She really didn't like it, but she endured the insult. Fortunately, as the wounds on her buttocks healed and she gained strength, the dysphagia was cured. Then Mama Jus was able to eat normally again.

It is reported that dysphagia often accompanies sickness or strokes in the elderly. It can lead to a pneumonia that is often fatal. So, keep a good eye on your charge.

See InformationResearchPro CD Category: Dysphagia

Dementia and Physical Deterioration

Some days are better than others, but the overall trend is downhill. That is the nature of ageing. Mental and physical health, sometimes one, sometimes the other and sometimes both lead to a downward spiral. And for the caregiver, the learning curve continues to rise. Over time, more and more mental and physical challenges and setbacks occur. It's just a fact of life.

What follows are snippets—little things that happen from day-to-day that reflect the diminishing health of the loved one and increasing challenges for the caregiver.

Mama Jus always like to read. Our home included built-in bookshelves that housed a wide assortment of books. One day I noticed that Mama Jus had selected a little book to read. Coincidentally, its title was *Justine*. I don't know why she chose it other than for the title, but she read on it nearly every day for a number of weeks.

At some point I realized that she had not read passed the first chapter. I asked what was so interesting about the first chapter of the book, and she replied with a smile, "I was just curious." I let it go at that.

Two years later I noticed that she was still reading the first chapter—I didn't say anything. But, I should have been more alert and perceptive. Why was she continuing to read the same material over and over? Surely it was a sign of something, but what?

This was before the days when one could "Google" just about anything to find out information. I wondered, was it a sign of mini-strokes or something else? Should I have called the neurologist? The answer is yes to all of the above. Maybe it was nothing, but maybe not. Investigate and get an answer when things like this occur. If what Mama Jus was doing was symptomatic, I could have had an answer almost immediately—either on the internet or from the neurologist. By being perceptive and acting quickly, one might avoid something serious. Be alert, and be proactive.

See InformationResearchPro CD Category:
Stroke, Dementia and Alzheimer's

In addition to the instance with the book, both my wife and I began to notice that Mom was experiencing periods of dullness. She did not seem alert, and her responses to our comments and questions were often met with a stare or a remark that was not responsive. The periods were usually short-lived, but they slowly became more and more frequent, and sometimes were more pronounced in depth and duration.

Don't assume anything. If there is a question about any behavior, get an answer. Again, whether it's from the internet or your family physician or neurologist, get an answer immediately. Of course the neurologist is my best choice.

See InformationResearchPro CD Category: Stroke

As time passed, probably into the third year, we began to notice that Mama Jus would walk out the front door and back in the side front door. Then she would continue to one of the back-porch doors, go out onto the porch and sit for two or three minutes and then get up and come back into the house through another back-porch door. Sometimes she would do this eight to ten times in a row, and then announce that she was retiring to her room. It wouldn't be long before she was back out of her room and making her circuits again.

Sometimes the routine would vary. Mama Jus would move from chair to chair—first in the living room and then in the den until she would make a similar announcement about retiring and go to her room.

We thought she was just restless or wanted to get some exercise. It seemed harmless, so we didn't question her.

Again, if your loved one exhibits any behavior that is the least bit questionable, get informed—get an answer. According to neurologists, any evidence of a stroke, large or small, should be attended immediately. You should know what to do. Be prepared to take quick action.

> *See InformationResearchPro CD Category: Stroke*

Hearing Loss

It became obvious that Mama Jus was losing her hearing. Was it a wax accumulation, ear nerve damage or other physiological impairment or was it from a stroke?

We tried to encourage Mom to get her ears tested to determine what was causing her hearing loss. Simple tests could tell whether the cause was wax blockage, structural deterioration of ear elements, nerve damage or brain damage from a stroke. Finally, we got Mama Jus past her apprehension about hearing aids, and she submitted to an ear exam. The ear doctor performed a thorough exam and concluded that a hearing aid could restore most of her hearing.

I went to two hearing aid retailers and retrieved their literature and videos. I presented them to Mama Jus and asked her to read the literature and watch the videos in her leisure.

After several days I caught Mom at a quiet moment and tried to engage her in talk about the hearing aid products. "Well, Mama Jus, what did you think about the video from the hearing aid company?"

"It didn't make much sense, and I don't want to use one!"

I did not realize that my efforts to help Mama Jus with her hearing had been preempted, but I should have. She had mentioned that friends at the Manor did not like their hearing aids and that they were too much trouble.

I should have enlisted some help from friends and family members who had positive results with their hearing aids. They could have told her that it was great to hear the birds again and to be able to hear the door-bell and the TV without turning the volume up high. And that it was nice not to have to ask others to repeat themselves; "What did you say?"

When I did raise my voice so she could hear, she would often say, "You don't have to yell at me."

I had no success with getting Mama Jus to obtain hearing aids, so her TV continued to blare, she couldn't enjoy the sounds of nature, and she continued to mis-understand what was said.

So, be smart about the way you manage your loved one's limitations. Think about the particular challenge and design a plan that is likely to succeed.

See InformationResearchPro CD Category:
Hearing, Elderly Diseases

Teeth

Mama Jus was fortunate. Her continuing practice of good oral hygiene prevented any serious problems with her teeth. She died with her own well-cared-for teeth in her mouth.

I know others will not be so fortunate. Do what you can to minimize dental problems with your own regimen of dental hygiene for your loved one.

See InformationResearchPro CD Category: Dental

Toenails

Fingernails are obvious, but toenails are not. Before I noticed, Mama Jus let hers grow until they curled under and made walking difficult. The ends of her toes were turning black from bruising.

When I noticed the problem, my wife suggested that we take Mama Jus to a Cosmetology School. What a great idea. The students need practice, so the schools offer treatments for a reduced fee. You can find them in the Yellow Pages or with an internet search.

I learned that the process includes soaking the nails in a solution to soften them, and then cutting them to an appropriate length. The toenail soaking solutions are available locally and it can be ordered on the internet and delivered to your door.

Although taking Mama Jus to the Cosmetology School worked well for us, I am advised that the more conservative approach is to contact a podiatrist—a foot expert. They can be found in the Yellow Pages or on the internet.

Make sure you check the nails frequently and prevent the 'Howard Hughes' syndrome.

> *See InformationResearchPro CD Category:*
> *Toenails*

Winding Down

Before Dad died, Mama Jus was always busy around the house, in the kitchen or out in the garden. She rose early, cooked for the boys and her husband, kept the house as neat as a pin and never spoke in anger or envy. To relax she sewed, hooked, read and even went to a health club for a year. Her social activities were a one-table (sometimes two-table) bridge game or lunch with a good friend.

It was such a contrast to see her physical health slowly fade and her interest in her friends pass away (as they passed away). Then it became, "I don't want to exercise, I don't want to cook and I don't want to go for a walk, I've never been able to just lie in bed. It is so wonderful and it feels so good." The downward spiral continued.

> *See InformationResearchPro CD Category:*
> *Depression*

Most of us have "senior moments," but it gets much worse. Whether related to Alzheimer's or old age senility, the short term memory can fail more and more frequently over time. At some point it leads to real dysfunction. You will hear comments like: Why did I come in here? What did you do with my furniture? Did you give my clothes away? I can't remember what I was getting ready to say. What's your son's name? Where did I put my purse? Is it time to go to bed (at nine in the morning)? When are we going to eat (just after breakfast)?

See InformationResearchPro CD Category: Alzheimer's, Dementia and Depression

As part of our plan to make Mama Jus feel good about her new surroundings, we knocked out one of the windows in her room and replaced it with a window box. She liked the idea and asked for a few plants as soon as we moved her into the house. Her choices were African violets, geraniums and ivy, and several little cacti, and a fern.

She really took good care of them for the first couple of years—they thrived under her care. But sometime after the second year, the plants began to droop and lose their color. Mama Jus insisted that she was caring for her plants every day, but the plants were signaling otherwise. It was a mystery.

It remained a mystery until one afternoon when I discovered Mama Jus spraying her plants. She methodically sprayed each plant, and then wiped the overspray off of the windows. It was then that I noticed that she was using disinfectant from the bathroom for her plants.

We talked about it, and she told me that she wanted the plants to have a little extra care. She wasn't sure why she had picked the disinfectant—"It was handy—right there under the bathroom sink."

Although Mama Jus seemed to understand the disinfectant was not for the plants, she continued to use it. We must have talked about it a dozen times, but to no avail. No matter where I put the disinfectant, she would find it and give her plants that "little extra care." The plants could only withstand so much care before they gave up the ghost.

See InformationResearchPro CD Category:
Dementia and Stroke

Untimely Events

I heard a noise in the house. I got up to investigate and found Mom in the living room with all of the lights on (4:15 AM).

I heard a TV blaring. I got up and found both the TV in the den and the one in Mom's room on with no one in either room (3:00 AM).

I heard a noise, got up and found Mom in the kitchen sitting at the breakfast table. The water is running in the sink and the refrigerator's door is open (1:45 AM).

I heard the front door close, so I got up to investigate. Mom was not in her room. I found her standing quietly on the front porch (2:35 AM).

So, what's a caregiver to do? For the TV, it's easy. Secure the remote—put it where Mom can't get it "after hours."

For the wandering, you will have to make a decision. And the choices are not fun, nor easy. Be aware that in some states it is illegal to lock someone in their bedroom, even for their own safety. If your loved one is prone to wander outdoors, investigate obtaining a tracking bracelet. Another option is to install sound alerts on targeted doors that sound when the door is opened.

If you come up with a solution, please let us know.
Post your solution on our blog:
www.dykepublishing.com/BLOG

Share solutions with others facing the same challenges.

See InformationResearchPro CD Category: Dementia

The Balancing Act—Independence and Capability

When your loved one gives up or loses some independence, the caregiver takes on what the elder gives up. It's also a psychological/emotional downer for both. It really is a balancing act. Let them keep as much independence as you dare—just watch it closely. I call it smart independence, or the ledger—what comes off their side moves onto your side.

So, physical activities, what to do when, what to wear, going out or staying in, making phone calls, operating the TV and so on are the things we take for granted. But at some point, your elderly parent or loved one needs help with almost everything. I suggest you let them keep as much independence as possible and practicable. Remember, if it comes off their side of the ledger, it goes onto yours. And the emotional consequences and time demands are not inconsequential for everyone.

At some point life doesn't get better with old age, it deteriorates. So, you have to anticipate that. Plan for the worst and hope for the best. Spend time preparing yourself every week. Read about Alzheimer's, read about incontinence, discuss and help your loved one prepare a living will. Stay ahead of the curve and your life and your eldercare will be what it should be rather than what it could have been.

Quick Check List

1)   Check all edges:
   - ✓   Feet
   - ✓   Knees
   - ✓   Hips
   - ✓   Shoulders
   - ✓   Hands
   - ✓   Elbow
   - ✓   Buttocks

2)   Stick out your tongue.
3)   Repeat after me:
   "The lazy brown fox jumped over the big blue duck."
4)   Smile for me.
5)   Wink at me with each eye.

Remember:
An ounce of prevention is worth a pound of cure!
You can't prevent it if you don't detect it!
And this takes less than a minute.
Do it every day.

PART 2: THE EMOTIONAL

I strongly suggest that you spend as much time as possible on this section of the book. The benefits for you, your loved one and every one else in the home will be both substantial and rewarding.

I am not the emotional type—at least I didn't think so. I was raised with two brothers (no sisters) in a household in which my dad made most, if not all, of the decisions. We hunted, fished, played golf, etc. and Mama Jus stayed at home. It was an old-fashioned male-dominated home. About the only emotions I experienced directly or indirectly were frustration and anger—the typical male emotions. But when my caregiving experience started, emotions fell on me like bricks—emotions that I had experienced infrequently.

Based on my experience, you will face an array of emotions when the care giving begins. It was the emotional stresses that came close to undoing me many, many times over the five-plus-year period that we cared for Mama Jus in our home. You will feel a variety of emotions during your caregiving experience, so I am doing all I can to prepare you.

How does one prepare for dealing with emotions? That is a question that I had never given any thought before our caregiving began. But I learned in a hurry that I was just as susceptible to emotions as anyone. And in retrospect, I know that I could have been prepared. So, to help you prepare, I am passing along to you my non-clinical discussion of emotions. Also, I am including a clinical treatment of emotions later in this book, an article called "Challenges and Choices: Elderly Caregiving," so you will have the benefit of trained professionals in the field of care giving.)

The experts who write about emotions, generally, and elder-care emotions, specifically, identify a number of emotions that affect both the caregiver and the care receiver. Those emotions include fear, worry, fatigue, sadness, isolation, frustration, anger, guilt, grief, and surprise/joy.

I found that the emotional part of care giving affects all involved in the process. Emotions are like high-energy balls—they can bounce from person to person to person gaining energy as they go. Even the bystanders are affected. So, it's best to recognize, understand and prepare for them for they will come your way from day to day.

Love

Caring for an elderly parent or loved one is truly a labor of love. Even if the primary reason for providing in-home eldercare is financial/economics, love had better be a large part of the equation. Without love, your challenges might prove to be insurmountable. (See: Chapter 6: *The Rewards of Eldercare*)

Fear and Worry

These two run together for me—they are about the same. Together they represent the unknown. *Am I doing a good job? Do I understand Mama Jus' needs? Am I being too restrictive and controlling? Is she happy living with us, or should I have left well enough alone? Am I making the correct conclusions about her health? Should I let her go to Houston or Homosassa to visit relatives? Will her relatives let her drink alcohol and smoke? Should I make her get more exercise? Am I equipped to recognize her medical needs? Am I reading her physical and mental symptoms accurately enough? Should I call her doctor about this or that? And, how does your loved one feel about these same things?* Common sense is the best measure, and it helps to have another opinion—my wife, my brother, my son, etc.

Fatigue

A little bit of this or that ever so often is OK, But, the constancy of bathing, cooking the meals, entertaining, exercising, doing the laundry *every day*, and supervising all activities is emotionally fatiguing. Without any help from other family members the demands sap your energy and make you susceptible to other more eruptive emotions. The emotional fatigue leads to physical fatigue. Help from others is essential, and vacations are a godsend.

Sadness

What has happened to my loved one? The changes in personality get so pronounced that you no longer recognize your loved one. You know he or she is your mom or dad, but they no longer act like them. It's like dealing with a stranger. What must they be feeling? Surely they see you differently, too. You know they must be weary of the old, worn body and the failing mind. They can no longer walk with you, let alone participate in more demanding activities. Their hearing is failing; their sight is failing; what about their taste, touch and smell? They must realize that they are dependent on another for most of their needs. It is sad for all.

Isolation

Before Mama Jus came to live with us (my idea), I was time rich and enjoyed activities with my family and friends. Almost all of that went away when I moved Mama Jus into our home. My wife was busy with her real estate brokerage, so "I was the man!" Day-after-day the duties were relentless. *Does anyone realize what I am going through? I can't do anything any more. I cannot go off and leave her alone in the house.*

Before Mama Jus' health and mind started to fail, we could visit about old times, current events and ideas. We could play cards or sit outside and watch the birds and squirrels. But as time wrought its toll, we could no longer do those things, and it was a matter of just being there.

I had to remember that the shoe was on the other foot when I was small, and Mama Jus had to attend to three of us. And back then, there were no "throw-away" diapers—they had to be washed. Three rambunctious boys must have been too much. But she did it! Day in and day out she did it. Mama Jus loved us and cared for us and now it was my turn. Just do it and be glad that you can return the love.

Frustration

For me, frustration is the trap, because right behind frustration is anger. They are like twins, except anger walks one step behind. Frustration never seems to last very long before anger raises its ugly head. For me, learning to recognize frustration was the challenge. If I could realize the signs of frustration, I had a chance of warding off anger. If not, I might say or do something out of anger that I would never do otherwise. Those angry words are often worse than slamming the door or stomping the foot. Remember: Learn to recognize emotions and deal with them appropriately.

If Mama Jus did not do what I expected her to do, I became frustrated. If I were kept from something I wanted to do, I became frustrated. Oh, those expectations! Expectation denied equals frustration, and we know that usually leads to anger. I had to learn to recognize the "expectation" scenarios, and act appropriately—it was hard.

Anger

Anger is the easy one, because it is so obvious. The challenge for me was to recognize my frustration before it morphed into anger. Mama Jus' anger was almost nonexistent. She wanted her cigarettes and nightly highball (or two or whatever she could beg, borrow or steal), but she didn't react outwardly with much anger when denied those things. She did better than I would have done under the same circumstances, I'm sure.

So, when golf, fishing or anything else that would have taken me from the house was in the offing, I had to remain vigilant, spot the rising frustration and ward off the anger. Sometimes it was easy and sometimes it was not. It's too bad it took so long for me to catch on to my susceptibility to emotions.

Guilt

My guilt usually came from doing what I thought I had to do to keep Mama Jus from getting out or getting into something. When her eating disorder developed, I had to keep her out of the refrigerator and the pantry. That meant locks on both, and frustration for Mama Jus when she couldn't get into either. It was that or she would eat constantly. Regardless, I felt guilty about it.

I had to put child-proof knobs over the door knobs on her bedroom door and the front doors. At times I had to keep her in her room or keep her from opening a front door to a stranger. That was the worst duty of all. I know it frustrated her, and I felt guilt.

Having to concentrate my time and attention on Mama Jus left little time for the rest of my family. That provoked a feeling of guilt.

And believe it or not, when I was relieved of my duty—when I was able to leave the house and play golf or fish or join other members of my family, I would feel guilty about just getting away for a while. Emotions are opportunists, so learn to recognize them and act appropriately.

Grief

When you see your loved one, your Mama Jus, with a blank stare;

When you see your Mama Jus asking for food when she just finished breakfast;

When you see your Mama Jus with her diapers half on and half off;

When you see your Mama Jus trying to work those stupid child-proof knobs;

When you see your Mama Jus take her last breath;

You will know grief...

Surprise / Joy

When the time comes when you've laid your loved one to rest, and you've past through your grief, you can reflect. If you can reflect and know in your heart that you've done all you could have to love and support your loved one to the end, you will experience surprise and joy. And it's the best. Not by your words, but by your actions, you have demonstrated your love and caring. You can forget all of the other emotions, and bask in real joy.

Antidotes

If you can learn to recognize emotions, you can respond appropriately. Work to recognize emotions at increasing levels of detail, and you can see the emotion coming, and act appropriately.

Other than learning to recognize emotions so you can act appropriately, I found another approach to be useful. When you fail to recognize the signs of an imminent emotion or when the emotion overwhelms you, use one of the antidotes below.

Before I learned to see them coming, I would just deal with my anger and disappointment after the fact. Usually the damage was already done to myself, my loved one or another in the house—I had already said unkind words or manifested my feelings in some untoward way. And always, I was ashamed and disappointed in myself. And it usually took minutes to an hour, if not a day or so, for the stress to subside. I had to do something. I had to establish a method to at least minimize my reactions and the ensuing stresses.

Research on the internet led me to a very useful set of antidotes to the emotions. First, my research led me to the writings of Robert Plutchik. He was a noted authority on emotions, and he developed a "Wheel of Emotions" in 1980. Robert Plutchik was a real pro in his field. He was professor emeritus at the Albert Einstein College of Medicine and adjunct professor at the University of South Florida. He received his Ph.D. from Columbia University and he was also a psychologist. He authored or coauthored more than 260 articles, forty-five chapters and eight books and has edited seven books. His research interests included among other topics the study of emotions and the study of the psychotherapy process. Plutchik's Wheel of Emotions included eight basic emotions and their opposites. They are:

Emotions

Basic	Basic's Opposite
Joy	Sadness
Acceptance	Disgust
Fear	Anger
Surprise	Anticipation
Sadness	Joy
Disgust	Acceptance
Anger	Fear
Anticipation	Surprise

He also recognized eight advanced emotions. The advanced emotions were comprised of two of the basic emotions. (Reference: Wikipedia, http://en.wiki pedia.org/wiki/Emotions.)

CONCLUSION

If you are unable to recognize an emotion, (i.e. "I don't know *how* I *feel!*"), refer to the lists of basic emotions and their opposites above. Use the emotional opposite of the emotion you are experiencing to help counteract the emotion you are experiencing. I can tell you this helps, and over time will help you recognize the early stages of an emotion and deal with it appropriately.

Remember, challenges grow over time and emotions do not disappear. So, start your effort to deal with emotions as soon as your loved one moves into your home, if not sooner.

See InformationResearchPro CD Category: Emotions

Chapter 5:

Eldercare from the Pros

To compare what I learned in my five and one-half years of in-home eldercare experience with what the professionals, the ones who have studied and written about eldercare and emotions, have to say, read this article written by Janet Clark and Katharine Weber, two women who have spent their careers teaching human development and family studies.

Challenges and Choices: Elderly Caregiving

Janet A. Clark and Katherine A. Weber

Department of Human Development and Family Studies

Reprinted with permission, Copyright 1996 University of Missouri Extension publication GH6657.

People are living longer than ever before. It has been estimated that the average American woman will need to provide about 18 years of some type of care for her elders. Because many women are marrying and having children later, they frequently find themselves in the sandwich generation, caring for their children and elders at the same time.

Family members provide approximately 80 percent of the necessary care for the elderly. Usually there is one primary caregiver and most often this is an adult daughter or spouse.

The primary caregiver frequently must provide this care under complex circumstances. Adult daughters often have to balance the concerns of their own immediate families, their work out-side the home, and their responsibilities for elderly caregiving.

If you are not currently caring for an elder, chances are that you will at some time during your life.

This guide provides information about our aging population, issues related to caregiving, ideas for taking care of yourself and resources that can help.

The aging population

The United States has been steadily aging for many decades. In 1900, about 3.1 million persons, or roughly 4 percent of the population, were aged 65 years and older. By 1990, the number of elderly persons had reached 31.2 million or 12.6 percent of the total population. This graying is expected to continue until at least the year 2040, when the elderly portion of the total U.S. population could total 22.6 percent.

Most dramatic is the increase in the oldest segment of society, those needing the most care. While the 65 to 74 age group is expected to increase by 17 percent between 1980 and 2000, the population over age 85 will more than double during this period.

In Missouri alone, the population of residents 85 years or older increased 33 percent between 1980 and 1990. The growth among the oldest-old is one of the results of improved health care and disease prevention techniques used in the United States during the 20th century.

Many older adults develop mental or physical impairments that will eventually cause them to need some outside help. In 1994, more than 6 million older Americans received some form of daily in-home care. Currently, half of the over-85 population needs some assistance with activities of daily living, such as eating, toileting or dressing. The availability of caregivers to the elderly is a critical factor in their being able to remain in the home, rather than having to be placed in an institution.

Although a caregiver can be anyone — a spouse, child, friend or neighbor, usually it is a woman. The typical caregiver is 57 years old, female, married and employed outside the home. She can expect to spend as many years caring for a parent as for her children. There is also a good chance that she will be a caregiver to more than one person during her lifetime.

While the number of older people is increasing, the pool of available caregivers for them is shrinking. Large numbers of women continue to enter the workplace, including those middle-aged women who are most often the caregivers to the elderly.

Also, those adults moving into the elderly age group have had fewer children, so there are fewer individuals to take on the caregiver role. The divorce rate has also had an effect. There are fewer spouses to provide care, and children often must care for divorced parents living in separate locations.

In addition, many of the females who are caregivers are fast approaching old age themselves. Because women are often younger at the time of marriage and generally outlive men, the caregiver in an older couple is likely to be the wife.

Thirty-five percent of caregivers are over age 65 and ten percent are over 75 years of age. These women are often called the hidden victims of caregiving because of their advanced age and the added strain of caring for another person.

What it means to be a caregiver

Caregiving can be defined as providing unpaid assistance for the physical and emotional needs of another person, ranging from partial assistance to 24-hour care, depending on his or her condition.

Caregivers can provide a wide range of services, depending on the degree of disability, economic situation and living environment of the older person. Outside help may or may not be involved. The person being assisted is the care receiver. This person may live with the caregiver or live elsewhere.

Quite often, as the disability increases, there is a progression in the amount of hands-on care that is needed, from assistance with daily living tasks to round-the-clock care. The type and amount of care will also vary with the type of disease or disability, that is, someone with Alzheimer's disease will have different needs than someone with cancer, for example.

Caregivers can also be considered primary or secondary. The person who has the main responsibility for the individual is the primary caregiver. Secondary caregivers offer support to the primary caregiver. If the primary caregiver is a daughter, the secondary caregivers tend to be the son-in-law and the grandchildren. While secondary caregivers are usually family members, they can also be friends or non-relatives. Secondary caregivers tend to be less involved in personal care of the elder, but help with transportation, shopping and home repairs.

Caregiving is an act of love — with consequences

Women have historically been presumed to be responsible for the well-being of their family members. In the past, the unmarried daughter was expected to provide care for an aging parent. Today, caregivers are overwhelmingly spouses and daughters. Women have at times been victim to what has been called the compassion trap. Their nurturing skills and sensitivity to others have made them more willing to take on difficult and often unrewarding personal duties.

Approximately two million women are part of the sandwich generation, caring for children and parents simultaneously. Working women have found that they must become skilled jugglers to meet all of the demands on their time.

The working woman who is also an elderly caregiver doubles up on her responsibilities and cuts back on her personal leisure time to fit everything in. Approximately 12 percent of women reported they needed to quit their jobs to fulfill their caregiving demands. Though most individuals take on the caregiving role willingly, Sommers and Shields in *Women Take Care* state that "caregiving is an act of love — with consequences."

Feelings experienced by a caregiver

Caregivers experience a wide range of feelings. Though most of them willingly choose to play a primary role in the care of their loved one, this role often carries with it conflicting emotions that must be dealt with. Among them:

Sadness and grief

Knowing that a person is in declining health and seeing it happen before your eyes can be difficult. Realizing that a loved one is suffering is often traumatic. Knowing that your husband, mother, sister, aunt or grandmother has a short time to live may cause you to begin grieving even before they die.

Fear and worry

Those of you who are taking care of someone in declining health may be plagued by fears. What will the future hold? How long will my loved one live? What if mother needs more care than I can give her? What if something happens to me, and I can't take care of her at all? How do I get extra help? Will we be able to afford this? Will I be able to hold on to my job or will they let me go? Will I have to quit? What if dad needs to be put in a nursing home — will I be able to do that?

Anger

Dealing with a loved one who is ill can be frustrating. Illness can affect people differently and some elderly persons may lash out at their loved ones out of their own fear, frustration, and growing dependency. The ill person might seem like a stranger. The caregiver needs to deal with her own anger; anger at the care receiver, at having to be the caregiver, at family members who may not be helping out, or at the doctors.

Guilt

The caregiver may feel guilty about many things, including guilt for not doing enough to change the situation or make the person happier, guilt for becoming angry with the ill person, for neglecting one's own spouse, children and other responsibilities. You may even feel guilty for enjoying time away from the loved one.

Fatigue

Being stretched in several directions can lead to fatigue. Caring for two households, caring for a person in ill health, dealing with the night-time wandering of an Alzheimer's patient and coping with incontinence are examples of things you may experience. In addition, having your own sleep interrupted regularly can lead to serious exhaustion. All of these things can last several months or even years.

Isolation

If you are the person primarily responsible for another's care, you may feel tied down and isolated. The person you're caring for might need to have someone nearby at all times, or simply not want to be left alone. Studies have indicated that caregivers experience a significant reduction in the amount of free time they have. You may feel that no one understands your situation or how you're feeling. It is important that you recognize these feelings of isolation and realize that they are normal.

Even though caring for an elderly person can be a stressful experience, it can also be a rewarding one for the caregiver. On the positive side, it can strengthen your relationships with your elders and give you a chance to get to know them better.

Providing assistance for your elders can give you the opportunity to express love and appreciation for the support that they have given to you. You can take great pride in the contributions that you are able to make at this time in their lives. Several studies have reported that when there is a strong bond established between the caregiver and the care recipient, caregivers feel less stress. Most older persons desire to have individuals in their family provide assistance to them and family members desire this as well.

A Caregiver's Bill of Rights
I have the right:

- ✓ **To take care of myself.** This is not an act of selfishness. It will give me the capability of taking better care of my relative.

- ✓ **To seek help from others** even though my relative may object. I recognize the limits of my own endurance and strength.

- ✓ **To take pride in what I am accomplishing** and to applaud the courage it has sometimes taken to meet the needs of my relative.

- ✓ **To protect my individuality** and my right to make a life for myself that will sustain me in the time when my relative no longer needs my full-time help.

You can add your own ideas to this list. Review it often!

Excerpted from "A Caregiver's Bill of Rights," Caregiving: Helping An Aging Loved One, by Jo Horne, AARP Books, 1985

Taking care of yourself

An important part of being a successful caregiver is remembering to take care of yourself. To provide effective care, you need to maintain your own health.

Neglecting yourself can have long-term consequences, not only for you, but for the person who needs your care. Adequate sleep and exercise, plus nutritious meals, are essential to your own well-being. Remember that the better care you take of your own health and emotions, the more you will be able to come through for the elderly person who needs you.

Taking time for yourself is also essential to your well-being. Helping an elderly person should not mean giving up all of your activities and relationships with other people. Give yourself a break from your caregiving activities by getting outside help.

Hire someone to stay with your elderly relative so that you can go out for lunch, go shopping or see a movie. Extended breaks, so that you can take a vacation or simply get some rest and relaxation, should be planned for as well. Perhaps a friend or another family member can take over for a while. Too frequently, caregivers are unwilling to ask for help because they think it may be a sign of inadequacy.

You may need to set limits on what you will do, difficult as this may seem. You cannot be expected to do it all. Other family members, even if they don't live nearby, can make a contribution. Community resources are available to help with many aspects of caregiving. Contact your local Division of Aging Office (DOA) and ask about local services. Or you can call the Missouri Information and Referral Hotline at 800-235-5503.

Many caregivers have found that organized support groups are helpful in dealing with the stress of caregiving. Attending an elder-care support group can give you a chance to share openly with other caregivers and to gain new ideas to help you manage your situation.

It's very important to have someone you can confide in and with whom you can share your true feelings. You can get information about local support groups by contacting a local hospital, home health agency or the Area Agency on Aging. Information on caregiving support groups is also available from Children of Aging Parents (CAPS) 215-345-5104.

It's a family matter

The need to provide care for an elder can happen suddenly or it can develop slowly. Your previously independent mother can fall and break her hip, or your father's diminishing eyesight can make it dangerous for him to continue to drive his car. If you are the oldest daughter or the child who lives closest to your parents, chances are you'll be the first to take action. Very soon, other family members may need to be contacted and become involved.

A major step toward family problem solving is for everyone to recognize that the caregiving responsibilities belong to all family members. Each person can do something, even if he or she lives at a distance.

The caregiving decisions that are made should focus on your elder's needs, perceptions and preferences. Usually, he or she will want to remain independent and in his or her own home as long as possible. Here are some of the services that might be available to your elders.

Potential services for the elderly

Household chores

High schools and colleges often keep lists of students who will do these chores for a small fee. Boy Scouts or 4-H groups may shovel snow or rake leaves as a service project for their organization.

Nutrition sites

Noon-time meals on weekdays are served in a central location such as a senior center or community center.

Home-delivered meals

This service is frequently called Meals on Wheels, and it provides a hot meal delivered to the home at noon, usually on weekdays.

Emergency response systems

Medic Alert and Lifeline are examples of commercial programs that provide different types of emergency service on a 24-hour basis.

Telephone reassurance

An individual calls an elderly person at a predetermined time each day.

Home health care

A variety of medical or personal care services can be brought into the home. Depending on the nature of the service, some may be covered by Medicare or other insurance plans.

Homeshare

A program through local family service agencies in which a group of older adults share a house or an apartment.

Adult day care

Supervised care, planned activities and health services are provided in a community facility for elderly citizens who would otherwise be at home, alone, during the day.

Group living facilities

Senior housing is frequently available that offers independent living along with central dining and various other support activities.

Long-distance care

Professional geriatric care managers can investigate options, provide guidance and supervision of an elderly person's care, if a family member does not live nearby.

Family communications

Getting all family members together for face-to-face communications is the best approach for decision-making. This meeting gives everyone the opportunity to discuss caregiving concerns, identify potential problems and solutions, and negotiate the sharing of the tasks.

It allows each family member the chance to clarify expectations and minimize any misunderstandings. Whenever possible, the elderly person who needs the additional care should be involved in the discussion. He or she has a right to participate in the decisions that affect him or her.

Family members may overestimate the older person's needs or they can make permanent decisions too quickly. While it's important to deal with the immediate problem, the family should take the time to explore various alternatives. Better solutions can be reached if there has been adequate time given to the decision making process and all family members have been involved.

Ideally, it would be better to plan ahead, before the crisis occurs. While it's difficult to talk about, find out what kind of care your elders might choose before they become ill or incapacitated.

This will give family members more time to look into the services available and what they will cost. With frequent changes in financial support through governmental programs, family members need to familiarize themselves with the latest policies.

Good advance planning can help bring peace of mind to you and your loved ones as you face this milestone in your lives together.

Key questions to ask service providers

✓ Is the agency licensed by the state?

✓ Are there other family caregivers who are willing to serve as references for the care facility?

✓ What is the range of services that is provided?

✓ When can family members visit and observe procedures in the care facility?

✓ What do the services cost?

✓ Will Medicare or other health insurance pay for the services?

✓ When and where are the services provided?

✓ What are the qualifications of the agency's employees?

✓ How are family members kept informed?

Resources

American Association of Retired Persons (AARP), 1909 K Street,
   NW, Washington, D.C. 20049. Request this free publication:
   Caregivers Resource Kit (D15267) 202-872-4700

Children of Aging Parents, 2761 Trenton Road, Levittown, PA
   19056 215-945-6900

Elder-care Locator Service 800-677-1116

National Family Caregivers Association, 9621 E. Bexhil Drive,
   Kensington, MD 20895 800-986-3650

National Council on the Aging, 600 Maryland Avenue, SW, West
   Wing 100, Suite 208, Washington, D.C. 20024 202-479-1200

Resource Manual: Information for Caregivers of the Elderly by
   Share Bane and Burton Halpert, Center on Aging Studies,
   University of Missouri at Kansas City 816-235-1747

Sandwich Generation, quarterly magazine, P.O. Box 132, Wick-
   atunk, NJ 07765-0132 908-536-6215

References

Brody, E.M. (1985). "Parent care as a normative family stress." *The
   Gerontologist,* 25, 19-29.

DeVaney, S.A. and Shrestha, L.B. (1995 Summer). "Our aging
   population and financing long-term care: Is long-term care insurance a reasonable solution?" *Journal of Family and Consumer Sciences,* 87, 21-25.

Duncan, S.F. (1994 Fall). "Coping with the stresses of caregiving."
   The Family Times newsletter. Montana Extension Service,
   Bozeman, MT.

Fengler, A.P. and Goodrich, N. (1979). "Wives of elderly disabled
   men: The hidden patients." *The Gerontologist,* 19, 175-183.

Frazier, Billie H. (1988). *Coping with caregiving — how to manage
   stress when caring for elderly relatives.* University of Maryland

Cooperative Extension Service, College Park, MD, Bulletin 326.

Ginsberg, S. and Galinsky, E. (Eds.) (1995 September). "Helping family caregivers care for themselves." *Work and Family Life* newsletter, 9, 4.

Ginsberg, S. and Galinsky, E., editors (1994 July/August). "Looking for local services for your older relatives? *Work and Family Life* newsletter, 8, 3.

Horne, J. (1985). *Caregiving: Helping an aging loved one.* AARP Books, Glenview, IL: Scott Foresman and Company.

Keith, C. (1995). "Family caregiving systems: Models, resources and values." *Journal of Marriage and the Family,* 57, 179-189.

Kramer, B.J. (1993). "Marital history and the prior relationship as predictors of positive and negative outcomes among wife caregivers." *Family Relations,* 42, 367-375.

Meyers, K. (1988). *Some facts on caring for elderly family members.* Minnesota Extension Service, Family Life Packets, Minneapolis, MN.

Michaels, B. and McCarty C. (1992). *Solving the work/family puzzle.* Homewood, IL: Business One Irwin.

Bane, S.D. (1992). *Caregiving for frail elders in rural America.* National Resource Center for Rural Elderly, University of Missouri-Kansas City.

Shapiro, B.A., Konover, V. and Shapiro, A. (1991). *The big squeeze: Balancing the needs of aging parents, dependent children and you.* Bedford, MA: Mills and Sanderson.

Sommers, T. and Shields, L. (1987). *Women take care: The consequences of caregiving in today's society.* Gainesville, FL: Triad Company.

Walker, A., Pratt, C., and Eddy L. (1995). "Informal caregiving to aging family members: A critical review." *Family Relations,* 44, 204-411.

The Rewards of Eldercare

When your loved one recognizes your help—your heart will soar.

When you realize that you have given your time unselfishly, it'll feel better than winning any race, contest, or trophy.

When your frustration morphs to anger, but you hold your tongue, you will feel triumph over self-centeredness.

When you change a parent's diaper, you will feel the satisfaction of repaying an old debt.

When you consider the safety devices you installed, you will recognize a job well done.

When guests have left the house, you will know that for just a little while your loved one has escaped the loneliness of old age.

When you make your loved one that special meal, you can reminisce about all of the wonderful meals you ate at her table.

When you handle the hassle of carting a wheelchair to the mall—you will know that you have knocked a hole in the boredom that "old folks" experience just about every day.

When you see a look of joy as your loved one interacts with children who have crawled up next to her on the couch, you will be reminded what a blessing children are.

When you persist and resist the unreasonable demands of your loved one, you can remember the times he or she helped you to develop good character.

When the final day comes that you put that beloved, used-up body and mind to rest, you will do so with a smile of fulfillment knowing you have satisfied the unspoken bond between child and parent.

Chapter 6:

The Rewards of Eldercare

What you have read in the preceding chapters is focused on the challenges of eldercare giving. But that is not the whole story. The rewards can far outweigh the challenges: demands on your time, emotional stresses, a drain on family resources and physical demands.

When your loved one recognizes your help—with getting dressed, or bathing, or eating or cleaning up after a disaster—and graces you with a little smile of acknowledgement that speaks without a word spoken, your heart will soar.

When you realize that you have given your time unselfishly for several days when your loved one is sick and needs all of your attention, the feeling ranks up there with the time you won a trophy for winning that race as a kid or that tournament as an adult.

When your frustration morphs into anger, but you hold your tongue, you will feel triumph over the self-centered part of your personality that was tempted to selfishly lash out at others, even those whom you love best.

When you change an adult diaper full of "you know what" without saying a word—thinking about all of your diapers that your loved one changed when you were a baby, you will feel the satisfaction of repaying an old debt.

When you look around the house at the devices on the doors, the cabinets and the refrigerator and know that you are keeping your loved one safe from others as well as herself, you will recognize a job well done.

When your guests have left the house and your loved one tells you what a great time she had, you will know that for just a little while she has escaped the solitude and loneliness of old age.

When you make your loved one that special meal, the one she has always enjoyed the most, you can reminisce about all of the wonderful meals you ate at her table.

When you push that wheelchair to the car, load your loved one and stow the chair, drive to the mall and unload the chair and seat your loved one and then stroll her by all of the windows so she can see the Christmas decorations, the mall's huge Christmas tree and the young folks shopping for all of those gifts they will give, and then return home, you will know that you have knocked a hole in the boredom that "old folks" experience just about every day.

When you see that look of engrossed joy as your loved one looks on at the small children that have crawled up next to her on the couch, you will no longer take for granted what a blessing our children are.

When you persist and resist the constant demands urged by the old habits of your loved one, you can remember the times that your loved one helped you overcome your tendencies to develop bad habits and encouraged you to develop good character.

And when that final day comes, you will be able to put that beloved, used-up body and mind to rest with a smile of fulfillment knowing that you have satisfied that unspoken bond between child and parent.

Good bye, Mama Jus . . . I love you.

Left: Tom, Mama Jus, Jessica, Sibyl, Kristin
Kathryn, James, Laura, 1985

Chapter 7:

The Role of the Secondary Caregiver
By Sibyl Dyke

In my role as secondary caregiver (spouse of the primary caregiver), I found that flexibility is key. The support needed by the number one caregiver will vary from day-to-day and from moment-to-moment. If the primary caregiver is male, in general more support may be necessary. Not only will it be important for the secondary caregiver to work diligently (and it *will* take work) on patience, compassion, tolerance and understanding for the one moving/living in, but for the primary caregiver as well. The role-reversal is difficult for both, and the input provided by the secondary caregiver—who is usually somewhat less emotionally involved—can set the tone for everyone. "Don't sweat the small stuff—and it's all small stuff" is the case in most instances. Focus on finding a *solution* rather than making an issue of the problem.

The life-style changes can, and most likely will, be challenging, i.e. entertaining in one's home may be difficult and going out for a time will, once again, require a sitter. Taking out the new resident may require a wheelchair—as opposed to the once-familiar baby stroller. (These are the same type of issues faced by those with special-needs children or adults with various physical and/or mental maladies.) Just plan ahead, allow extra time and be sure to remind the primary caregiver to have all necessary supplies (including a cell phone) on hand if you aren't accompanying them on an outing.

Encourage the primary caregiver to take advantage of special occasions to share time and loving moments with your special "guest." (For purposes of this book, I will refer to this person as "parent.") A trip to the mall to see Christmas decorations, the christening of a grandchild, a picnic in the park on a beautiful day, attendance at a concert or church service can be especially meaningful and can bring back memories of "the old days" and emphasize the happy moments of this relationship. Times such as these lessen the stress and tension that are frequently felt by the primary caregiver during day-to-day duties and emphasize the positive aspects of in-home care.

Suggest that your primary caregiver address end-of-life issues ahead of time. If appropriate, input should be solicited from the parent and discussed with all involved. This alleviates any doubts that the primary caregiver might have regarding whether his decisions are the correct ones and relieves him of making such decisions during increased emotional stress.

Encourage family gatherings at home in which all age groups can participate and have fun. If appropriate, old friends of the parent can be included. As time goes by and these activities become more difficult—mentally/physically—it may be comforting to the parent to recall these occasions. This also helps to bring perspective to other generations that might be there during the gatherings and allows them to experience the pleasure of brightening the day of someone who has been a part of their life.

Most importantly, be available to take-over the primary role on a routine basis so that the primary caregiver can have time off. In addition, make arrangements for you and your primary caregiver to have substitute (respite) care available so you can both take off at the same time. If appropriate, encourage the primary caregiver to make arrangements with other family members to accept this responsibility for periods of several days at a time at routine intervals—bimonthly, annually—whatever works for them, and for the both of you.

Articles, Information and Products Accessible Using the Enclosed CD:

Alcohol, Alzheimer's and Dementia, Anger, Arthritis, Asset Management, Bank Accounts and Banking, Bedsores, Blogs, Bowel Dysfunction, Brain Fitness and Neuroplasticity, Cancer, Caregiver, Caregiving, Constipation, Dental, Depression, Diabetes, Diet, Dementia, Driving, Drugs and Drug Plan Benefits, Dysphagia, Education, Eldercare, Eldercare Blogs, Elderly's Diseases, Emotions, Exercise, Eyesight, Feelings of the Caregiver, Hearing, Hispanic–Problems Peculiar to Hispanics, Humor, Incontinence and Constipation, Insomnia, Insurance Products, Internet, Law, Living Wills, Long-Term Care, Medicaid, Medicare, Medigap (Medicare Supplemental), Mental Health, Music and the Elderly, Neuroplasticity, Products for the Elderly, Prostate Disorder, Safety, Senior Citizens, Skin, Smoking, Social Security Benefits, Spirituality, Stroke, Swallowing Disorder, Toenails, Urinary Tract Infection, Vision, Wills/Trusts

Appendix:

Resource Guide and Products for the Elderly

Links to the following information may be found at

DykePublishing.com/eldercareinformation

on the enclosed

InformationResearchPro–ProductResearchPro CD.

Because we are supporting our *Information Research Pro* and *Product Research Pro* from our website, DykePublishing.com, our search results will always be current. Any information that drops off of the internet for any reason or error links will be excluded from search results for both information and products. Also, new information and products will be added, so your copy of the CD will always be a helpful, timesaving and current resource.

Dyke Publishing is committed to helping you care for your loved one and to that end the *Mama Moves In* package (book and CD) will always be up-to-date.

Resource Guide

ALCOHOL

"Alcohol and the Elderly": MC Dufour, L. Archer, E. Gordis, Clin Geriatr Med. 1992 Feb; 8(1): 127-41; National Institutes of Health

"Alcoholism in the Elderly" : Sally Rigler, M.D. of the University of Kansas School of Medicine (*American Family Physician*; March 2000)

ALZHEIMER'S AND DEMENTIA

(See also: Mental Health.) (See also: Law (below).)

Alzheimer's Association

Alzheimer's/Dementia News

Alzheimer's Foundation of America

Find Eldercare Providers in Your State

"Is It Alzheimer's Disease?": Johns Hopkins Health Alerts

The Mind and Moods of the Aging by BJ Gurland (Routledge; New York and London 1983)

ANGER

The Encyclopedia of Aging and the Elderly: MedRounds.org

"Dealing With Anger and Eldercare Abuse: Communicating with the Person in Your Care is Angry": Livingston County (NY) Office for the Aging

ARTHRITIS

American Arthritis Foundation Elderly Exercise

"Arthritis in the Elderly":Professor John Murtagh, Professor of General Medicine, Monash University, Melbourne, Australia (1995)

"Arthritis in the Elderly": University of Wisconsin (4/10/2008)

ASSET MANAGEMENT

"Asset Management": Frank, Frank and Scherr, LLC, an Elderlaw Practice *(brief and to the point)*

"Elderly Asset Management": Jonathan S. Feinstein, Yale School of Management and Ching-Yang Lin, Department of Economics, University of Wisconsin *(very detailed and technical)*

"Elderly Asset Management and Health: An Empirical Analysis": Jonathan Feinstein, Yale and Chih Chin Ho (Internal Revenue Service) *(Abstract of the article with link to full article)*

BANK ACCOUNTS AND BANKING

"Frauds that Target the Elderly": Washington State Department of Financial Institutions

See Asset Management above.

BEDSORES

"Bed Sores": The University of Virginia Health Center

"Bed Sores—Not always a sign of neglect": Dr. Michael Hochman, *Boston Globe*

Definition of Bedsores
Information and resources

Blogs
See also Eldercare Blogs

The Eldercare Diary: This is a great site. The owners have or have had all four parents in their home during the last four years, and they share their experiences.

Introduction to the Veterans' Aid and Attendance Improved Pension—This site publishes an article that describes a financial assistance plan for veterans and their wives. It also offers a blog for eldercare.

Welcome to the 25th Eldercare ABC Blog Carnival—this site lists and gives access to a number of eldercare blogs.

BOWEL DYSFUNCTION

Bowel dysfunction: Family Village in Wisconsin *(contacts, networking, links, information)*

"Managing bowel dysfunction in the elderly": Clinical Center of The National Institutes of Health

National Multiple Sclerosis Foundation

BRAIN FITNESS AND NEUROPLASTICITY
(rehabbing the brain after strokes)

"Brain changes from meditation": A study from the University of Wisconsin, Madison

Exercises and work for the brain—keep it active—use it or lose it: Software programs

"Introduction to neuroplasticity": MemoryZine

Neuroplasticity (brain plasticity)—what is it and
   how it works

"Neuroplasaticity and the Brain that Changes Itself":
   Laurie Bartels, Nov. 12, 2008, SharpBrains

Rehabbing the brain after strokes

"Scientists Investigate Brain-Healthy Practices":
   Brain Fitness Channel

"Steps to Maintain Brain Fitness": Third Age

"Tapping brain plasticity for stroke rehab": The
   Brain Science Podcast with Dr. Ginger Campbell

Vision loss from stroke, fighting back,
   neuroplasticity

CANCER
"Financial Assistance": Cancer*Care*

CARE-GIVER
"Challenges and Choices: Elderly Caregiving":
   Janet A. Clark, Katherine A. Weber, Department
   of Human Development and Family Studies.
   *This information is for the caregiver. It is a must
   read for those considering moving an elderly parent
   into their home.* (Article is reprinted in *Mama
   Moves In* with permission.)

CAREGIVING
Spirituality and Aging: *This site is a must for all
   caregivers! It is full of resources on may topics germane to the task of good caregiving.*

CONSTIPATION

(See also: Incontinence.)

"Constipation and Caloric Intake in the Elderly": JournalWATCH, August 2, 1994

"Constipation and the Elderly": Medline *(members only)*

"Constipation in the Elderly": Ariba Kahn, M.B.B.S. and John e. Morley, M.D.

"Constipation in the Elderly": David C. Schaefer, M.D., Ph.D., Lawrence J. Cheskin, M.D., Johns Hopkins University School of Medicine, published by The American Academy of Family Physicians

"Little Known Ways to Prevent Constipation in the Elderly": Tracy S. Hill

"Using fiber to Control Constipation in the Elderly—Geriatric Nutrition": *Nutrition Research Newsletter, Oct. 2003*

White Paper: Pain Free in One Day *(Commercial site)*

DENTAL

Care Giving and Elderly Dental Care: Caregiver's e-Mall

"Daily Dental Care Tips for Those Caring for the Older Adult": *Great information source about brushing and flossing and warning signs, and more…*

"Dental Care for the Elderly": Virginia Department of Health

"Dental Care Savings for Seniors"

Dental Plan (commercial site, Texas)

"Don't Let Elderly Dental Care Fall Through the Crack"

"Implications of access, utilization and need for oral health care by the non-institutionalized and the institutionalized elderly on the dental delivery system": TA Dolan and KA Atchison. *Journal of Dental Education*

DEPRESSION

"Depression—Elderly": National Institutes of Health

"Depression in the Elderly—Signs and Symptoms"

"Depression in the Elderly": Web MD

"Risks of Depression in the Elderly": National Institute of Mental Health

DIABETES

"Complications of Diabetes in Elderly People" Edward W. Gregg, Epidemiologist, *British Medical Journal*

"Diabetes Affects Bones in the Elderly": American Diabetes Association

"Diabetes in the Elderly": *Diabetes Life*

"Elderly with Diabetes Face Treatment Challenges": Dr. Jeffrey Halter, Director of the Geriatrics Center and Institute of Gerontology, The Internet Journal of Geriatrics and Gerontology

"Management of Diabetes in the Elderly" Jeffrey I. Wallace, MD, MPH, University of Washington Department of Medicine

DIET

Diet and Weight Control

Eating right—alkaline compounds whether from fruit and vegetables or supplements may counteract bone density loss

Keep Diet High in Fiber and Water

Mediterranean Diet Aids Aging Brain

DRIVING

Driver Safety and Mobility Options (numerous articles from AARP, a good resource)

Warning Signs and Helping and Unsafe Driver to Stop Driving: *much information*

When to Put the Brakes on Elderly Drivers: *includes a checklist*

DRUGS and DRUG BENEFIT PLANS

A guide to Medicare and drug plans from Coventry Health Care

Great prices on mail order drugs from Canada

Private drug plans and drug benefit plans

U.S. Government Medicare site

DYSPHAGIA

Article featuring description of symptoms and ramifications of the disorder

Brief abstract

Dysphagia research meeting—report

EDUCATION

Alcohol Education Effective with the Elderly: jointogether.org

New Careers and Education: LifeInTheUSA.com

Online Education for the Elderly: GoArticles.com *(good information about how and where, etc.)*

ELDERCARE

American National Red Cross offers new guide for family care giving *(Guide and DVD)*

American Red Cross: Home Care for the Elderly

Eldercare: Preserving Your Marriage and Family *(second article on the page)*

Eldercare—support groups, services and solutions:

"Challenges and Choices: Elderly Caregiving:" by Janet A. Clark and Katherine A. Weber both of the Department of Human Development and Family Studies. (Missouri University Extension) *A scholarly article I have reprinted with permission in* Mama Moves In.

Family Care Giving Guide and DVD from the American Red Cross: For product information contact Customer Service at 1-866-632-7751 Monday – Friday 9 am - 9 pm EST or email customerservice@redcrossstore.org. Use Product Code Number: RC653975.

ELDERCARE BLOGS

See also Blogs

Jack Halpern, advocate for the elderly

Elder-caregivers community

Latest news and happenings related to eldercare

ELDERLY'S DISEASES

Alzheimer's, depression, heart disease, Osteoarthritis, Osteoporosis, Longevity, plus Senior Health Basics: *another commercial site, but much good information*

Righthealth.com: *a commercial site, but full of information about many diseases—explore the many available links*

EMOTIONS

Centre for Vital Elders. *This site offers a wealth of articles from 12 categories of emotions.*

Coping with Your Difficult Order Parent: Grace Lebow and Barbara Kane *(gives insight and methods for coping with eldercare)*

Dealing with Family Denial. *Clear communication among family members is key to the success of a family plan.*

"Home Health, Hospice and Elder Care: Grief and Loss": The University Hospital of Columbia and Cornell

Learning To Recognize Emotions and Dealing With Them Appropriately: *List of emotions as compiled by many of the recognized experts in the field as well as a tree structure by Parrot (2001). It also references researched explanations of many forms. Great detail/depth.*

Robert Plutchik's "The Nature of Human

Emotions," *Science* Week 3 August 2001. *From UCLA's Education Department, an interesting discussion*

EXERCISE

The Benefits of Daily Exercise for the Elderly—Avoid Chronic Disease: Suite 101.com

"Exercise Can Help Elderly Avoid Devastating Falls" MSNBC, March 20, 2007 *(anecdotal—good account)*

"Exercise for Adults and the Elderly": ACS News Today, American Cancer Society *(help build red blood cells and strengthen the immune system)*

"Exercise for the Elderly" from Family Doctor.org *(good article with pictures for the recommended exercises)*

"Elderly Improve with Exercise": United States Department of Agriculture

"Fit, Not Frail: Exercise as a Tonic for Aging": Jane E. Brody, June 24, 2008, *The New York Times. (Good practical information—why, how and what kinds of exercise to do)*

EYESIGHT

"15 Tips on Aiding People with Poor Eyesight": Randy Walden, CSA (Certified Senior Advisor)

A Little Humor for the Elderly

"Active Life Helps Eyesight in the Elderly": August 23, 2008

Active Life Helps Eye Sight of the Elderly—

Reducing the Risk of Macular Degeneration (Doctor NDTV)

"Oily Fish May Protect Eye Sight in Elderly": UPI.com, August 11, 2008

FEELINGS OF THE CAREGIVER

"The Caregiver Has Feelings, Too": *See this site for a comprehensive statement about the feelings that a caregiver will experience. Reprinted with permission in* Mama Moves In

Dealing with Anger and Resentment: Dealing with Siblings

HEARING

Elderly Hearing Aid Users Share their Experiences from Hear-It.org *(16 pertinent selectable articles)*

Hearing Loss Among Elderly May Be Linked to Brain Function: McKnight's Long Term Care News

HISPANIC—PROBLEMS PECULIAR TO HISPANICS

A Safe Heaven for My Abuleita

Family and Community Medicine

Hispanic elderly

HUMOR

Daily Humor for the Elderly

Elderly Jokes: Irondequoit Catholic Communities

INCONTINENCE AND CONSTIPATION

Common problems in the elderly: constipation, dementia and incontinence—tips for the caregiver

Urinary Incontinence in the elderly:

Urinary Incontinence in women—detailed and technical information (plus a slide show)

Urinary tract infection in the elderly

INSOMNIA

"Insomnia in the elderly—treatment could improve mental and physical health": The American School of Professional Psychology

Sleep problems: generally

Sleeping well—Healthy habits to reduce sleep problems and prevent insomnia

INSURANCE PRODUCTS

Insurance products for the elderly

INTERNET

Easy to Use Computer for Seniors: bigscreenlive.com)—*good product for the elderly with a free 30-day trial*

Seniors Using the Interne: The Henry J. Kaiser Foundation (.org))

Visually impaired elderly using the internet

LAW

American Bar Association answers frequently asked
  questions about Law and the Elderly

Commission on Law and Aging: American Bar
  Association

Deducting Care of the Elderly

Elderly Tax Deductions

How to Take Tax Deductions for Eldercare

"Law, The Legal Needs of the Elderly Give Rise to
  New Specialty": *The New York Times*

Taxes and Alzheimer's (Alzheimer's Association)

Tax Deductions and Credits Regarding Alzheimer's:
  Alzheimer's Association

LIVING WILLS

"The Living Will: A Guide To Health Care Decision
  Making": *Written by a doctor and an attorney,
  Jack P. Freer and Elizabeth G. Clark, respectively,
  who have covered all the bases. I highly recommend
  your reading this article.*

Living Wills and Healthcare Power of Attorney:
  *This site can help you find an attorney who can
  help you with Living Wills*

Making a Living Will Online: *As competent adults,
  we have the right to make decisions in advance as to
  whether to decline life support when it's clear that
  death is imminent or a state of coma becomes
  permanent. A Living Will is a document which lets
  you decide whether or not to be kept on artificial
  life support. These documents may also appoint*

someone to make health care decisions on your behalf in case you are unable to do so.
Living Wills and Advance Directives for Making Medical Decisions (Mayo Clinic staff)
Living wills are one part of advance directives and describe your treatment preferences in end-of-life situations. Unexpected end-of-life situations can happen at any age, so all adults need advance directives.

The U.S. Living Will Registry: *What good is a Living Will if it cannot be found when needed? The U.S. Living Will Registry offers an online service by which one can register Living Wills and have them accessible online to doctors, hospitals, etc. when needed.*

LONG-TERM CARE

Genworth Financial Cost of Care Survey—*Covers All 50 States—go to this site to get costs for long-term costs in many cities of all 50 states: An excellent site for cost information*

MEDICAID

Medicaid and Medicare **by ZIP CODE:** Search For Information On Both Medicaid and Medicare By Your ZIP Code
Medicaid site for Texas
Medicaid: Wikipedia's definition

MEDICARE

Medicare and Medicaid by ZIP CODE: *Search For Information On Both Medicaid and Medicare By Your ZIP Code. Also, Get Answers To Your Medicare Questions.*

U.S. Government Medicare site. *Find out about Parts A and B, and what you must own to qualify for Medigap (Medicare Supplemental Insurance).*

MEDIGAP (Medicare Supplemental)

Medigap (Medicare Supplemental Insurance)— A Medigap policy is health insurance sold by private insurance companies to fill the "gaps" in Original Medicare Plan coverage. Generally, when you buy a Medigap policy you must have Medicare Part A and Part B. You will have to pay the monthly Medicare Part B premium. In addition, you will have to pay a premium to the Medigap insurance company.

MENTAL HEALTH

"Dementia": The Journals of Gerontology:

Elder Depression—abuse—law firm reference

"Mental Health and the Elderly": (Argosy University) The American School of Professional Psychology. *A wide range of articles searchable by category*

"Mental and Physical Problems of the Elderly"—*this was a "Google" search criteria, which resulted in about 1,530,000 articles—too numerous for practical reasons*

"Psychiatry of the Elderly": World Health Org.

MUSIC AND THE ELDERLY

"Long Term Effects—Elderly, Even with Dementia, Maintain Better": *Journal of Music Therapy*

"Music Helps the Elderly Sleep Better": *Medical News Today*

NEUROPLASTICITY

See: Brain Fitness.

PRODUCTS FOR THE ELDERLY

See extensive section that follows in this Appendix.

PROSTATE DISORDER

"Prostate Disorder": Johns Hopkins. To order a free *Johns Hopkins Guide to BPH Disorder*

SAFETY

See the U.S. Consumer Product Safety Check List in Chapter 3. Also see the category "Safety" on the Products Research Pro CD included with this book.

SENIOR CITIZENS

For All Things Senior: From Products And Services To Housing To Articles On All Topics Germaine to Seniors and Senior Health Care/Caregiving Covering the United States And Canada— A Quarterly Magazine

SKIN

"Paper Thin Skin Tears Easily": Dermatology Blog
"Skin tears—the enemy of frail skin": *Health Care Industry Magazine. All about elderly skin, tears, causes, prevention and treatment.*

SMOKING

"Disease consequences more likely to affect the elderly": National Institutes of Health

"Information on Tobacco and Older persons": The Center for Social Gerontology

"Smoking contributes to mental decline in the elderly": from a study released at the 50th anniversary meeting of the National Academy of Neurology (April 1998)

SOCIAL SECURITY BENEFITS

Good information on many topics from Wikipedia
Publications from the Social Security Administration
U.S. Government site

SPIRITUALITY

Spirituality and Aging: *A must for all caregivers. Whether spiritual or not, you can find interesting thoughts and ideas that might help you with your care giving. It covers many topics and is in contradistinction to religion. It is worth a look, if not serious study, as a resource.*

STROKE

Information about strokes—updated information

Learn about micro strokes—information as well as videos

Micro strokes—a warning

Preventing and treating strokes: Harvard Medical School

Tests for a stroke

Web site for the American Stroke Association, a division of the American Heart Association

SWALLOWING DISORDER

See: Dysphagia above.

TOENAILS

"How To Cut Your Toenails": Fred Beaumont, Institute of Chiropodists and Podiatrists

URINARY TRACT INFECTION

Urinary Tract Infection (Agri-Life Extension, Texas A&M System)

VISION

Vision issues and information: newsletter, product referrals

WILLS/TRUSTS

Legal Counsel for the Elderly": University of Alabama Law School

See also: Asset Management above.

Products for the Elderly

The following commercial websites are offered as a convenience and are included on the enclosed ProductResearchPro section of the resource CD for one-click access on the internet under:

DykePublishing.com

Listed for each site are the general product categories and sub-categories within which are include *many* products for the elderly. Hundreds of products are available from the online product stores, and it is worth the time to browse through the sites if only to see what is available to improve the quality of life for your loved one, and ease the workload for the caregiver. Some of these products are quite ingenious and most are very useful for particular needs.

Use your ProductResearchPro CD to search under categories and sub-categories. You will find that the highly organized format makes the products for which you shop easy to find. And, you will be given choices so you can compare brands and prices.

DISCLAIMER: Neither *Mama Moves In*, nor its author nor its publisher are responsible for or accept liability for any of the products sold at the referenced sites or other sites found in your searches.

What you see below, sites, product categories and sub-categories, are examples of sites, product categories and sub-categories that you will find as you search using the program on your ProductResearchPro CD. Just insert your ProductResearchPro CD in your computer and it will open and run automatically.

Allman Products

Categories: Back Support Cushions, Bathing Accessories, Bed Accessories, Crutch Accessories, Cushions, Donut Rings, Foam Wedges, Incontinent Pants, Pillows & Neck Support Cushions, Walkers and Wheelchairs, Wheelchairs & Walker Accessories

American Printing House for the Blind

Categories: Audio Equipment, Books & Magazines, Braille Reading & Writing, Computers & Software, Electronics, Games-Puzzles-Toys, Cards, Low Vision Reading & Writing, Maps & Globes, Measuring Devices, Organization Products, Orientation & Mobility, Tactile Learning Products, Transition & Career Education, Videos

Caregiver Products

Categories: Gadgets, Kitchen, Getting ready, Around the House, On the Move, For Your Comfort, Arthritis Supplies, Mobility Aids

Comfort Plus Products

Categories: Adjustable Beds, Bath Aids, Chairs, Walkers, Scooters, Powerchairs, Wheelchairs, Accessories

Dynamic-Living

*Categories on this site are defined by **use** or by location.*

By Use: Moving Around, Sitting Around, Hands, Vision, Hearing, Communicating, Caregiving, Memory, Generously Sized, Reaching, Gifts

By Location: Car, Bathroom, Shower & Tub, Toilet, Medicine Cabinet, Dressing Room, Bedroom, Kitchen, Dining Room, Family Room, Kid's Corner, Tool Shed

Eldercare Products

Categories: Bath, Bed, Caregivers' Corner, Clothing, Dining, Gift Shop, Incontinence, Mobility, Vision/Hearing

Elder Depot

Categories: Bed, Bath, Clothing, Dining, Incontinence, Vision/Hearing, Mobility

First Street Online

Categories: Features Products, Home Solutions, Healthy Living, Electronics & Gadgets, Unique Gift Ideas

The Scooter Store

Categories: Scooters, Power Chairs, Lift Chairs, Lifts, Wheelchair Ramps, Rehab Products

Independent Living Aids

Categories: Books, Calculators, Canes & Mobility, CCTV's, Clocks & Timers, Assistive Technology, Durable Medical Supplies, Electronics, Games, Health Care, Household, Lamps, Magnifiers, Talking, Telephones, Watches, Writing & Record, Keeping and Money Management

Senior Super Stores

Categories: Assisted Hearing, Assistance Devices, Bathing & Grooming, Bathrobes, Books, Clothing, Cookbooks, Footware, Health, Hobbies & Gardening, Household, Incontinence products, Kitchen, Leisure, Mobility, Seat Lifts, Peripheral Neuropathy, Phones & Pagers, Safety, Skin Care, Sleepware, Sporting Goods, Support Hosiery, Support Products, Travel, Women's Health

Acknowledgments

I acknowledge the patience and understanding my wife, Sibyl, has allowed me during the writing of *Mama Moves In.* Additionally, I thank her for her memory, critiques and proof reading.

I thank Don R. Walker of Austin, Texas, with Physicians Mutual for coaching me about the terms used in the eldercare insurance industry. Based on his experience and achievement of being in the top twenty agents at Physicians Mutual for the last five years, he has helped me understand the concepts and costs of Medicare Supplemental, the Drug Plans that supplement Medicare, and Long Term Care.

I give special thanks to the Missouri University Extension for allowing me to reprint and include in its entirety "Challenges and Choices: Elder Caregiving" by Janet A. Clark and Katherine A. Weber.

I also thank Yokima Cureton and Genworth Financial for allowing me to include forms, facts and figures researched and published on Genworth's website. Additionally, I thank Genworth for allowing my readers to directly access Genworth's website using the Information Research Pro CD to find annual eldercare costs for most cities in all states of the United States on Genworth's interactive map of the United States.

I thank the U. S. Consumer Products Safety Commission for allowing me to reprint and include in its entirety the "Home Safety Check List."

My highest praise I give to Janice Phelps Williams, my book designer, inside and out, editor–in-chief, proofreader, illustrator, copy writer and coach. Her experience and keen insights kept the book on track, on time and within budget.

RS Design Group brings to my humble table everything technology. RS Design's chief, Rich Siglin, is The Man. He brings it from inside the box, on the box and, most importantly, outside the box. He has graced me with all of his knowledge, skills and imagination. I finally have an association with a man who's turf spans mainframes, internet and PC's, data analysis and integrations of every type, and programming in everything from machine language to the latest programming language frameworks that make beautiful web pages. Those web pages utilizing "Cloud" and "Mashup" technology make "real-time" a reality and combine to birth the finest websites on Earth, bar none. Demonstrating profound patience and a kind persona, Rich enables me to market and sell my book and all of the information and product research services that go with it. He gives my business plan the best probability of success.

My Father in Heaven is my Supreme Enabler.

About the Author

After earning his J.D. from The University of Texas Law School in August, 1967, Tom practiced law at Fulbright & Jaworski in Houston, Texas, for two years doing estate, trust and probate, tax and general litigation work. He was hired away by West Park Industries, a manufacturing company building its own product lines and doing contract machine work for both private industry and the United States government, as house counsel in 1970.

One year later Tom was made president and CEO of the company. His duties included manufacturing, finance, law, and management of up to fifty employees plant-wide. The manufacturing processes included production and quality control of as many as twenty thousand units per week from production lines running twenty-four hours per day, six days per week.

Although Tom's business interests precluded a full time law practice, he continued to involve himself in the legal profession over the years by managing the legal affairs of his family's businesses including several major litigations. Tom used the computer in the management of his family's real estate business, his law practice, and his analysis of financial and commodities markets.

The author formed a litigation support firm that operated in the 1990s providing litigation support to both law firms and corporations. The firm built large databases, abstract, full-text and image, for searching all of the documents in litigation matters. His primary client was Exxon, USA.

He wrote marketing pieces and technical manuals for each of the companies for which he worked.

B.B.A.(General Business), the University of Texas at Austin, June, 1963; J.D., The University of Texas Law School, August, 1967 (Texas Law Review candidate).

Nothing in his business career prepared him for eldercare.

Index

QUICK ORDER FORM

Postal orders: Send your check or money order to the address below.

Dyke Publishing Company
THOMAS DYKE, #307
5501-A BALCONES DRIVE
AUSTIN, TEXAS 78731, USA.

Please send _____ copy(ies) of _Mama Moves In_ (book plus CD) at $24.50 per copy*

Name: _____

Address: _____

City: _____

State: _____Zip: _____

Telephone: _____

Email address: _____

*Add to the Sales Price of _Mama Moves In_:

    Sales tax: Please add 8.25% for products shipped to Texas addresses.

    Shipping and handling: $4.10 (1st book) and $2 for each additional book.

    Outside of the Continental U.S.:

    Email orders@DykePublishing.com for costs.